THE STORY OF EYES

THE FRONTISPIECE—The story of sight, and of its effect upon various animals, is like an increasingly spectacular pageant, covering vast stretches of time. It begins with minute living creatures of the ocean, their entire bodies sensitive to light, and continues through definite eyespots, such as can be seen on the ray-tips of starfish, to the more complete eyes of vertebrate fish. Scorpions—ancestors of all insects—were the first to look upon dry land. The many-faceted, mushroom-like orbs of certain insects are typified in the picture opposite, just below the cross section of a human eye, by the eyes of a dragonfly. Later, the splendid vision of birds appears, represented here by a vulture; and long, long after that come our own eyes, whose limitations we know, but whose future is uncertain.

The Story of
EYES

BY S. SUTTON-VANE

Illustrated by
ANTHONY RAVIELLI

New York • THE VIKING PRESS

Library of Congress catalog card number: 58-7073
Lithographed in U. S. A. by Murray Printing Co.

To M. G.

For her unfailing awareness

The author wishes to express appreciation
to David A. Bardack; to Mary B. Patsuris,
scientific assistant, Department of Geology
and Paleontology, the American Museum of
Natural History; and to Dr. William K.
Gregory, Curator Emeritus of Fishes and of
Comparative Anatomy at the Museum, for
their helpful criticism of this book.

Contents

Author's Note

THIS book is the result of a layman's sudden curiosity about an asset most of us take for granted. In the course of conversation one night, a few friends and I discovered that we knew next to nothing about our own eyes —we did not know how they originated, how they work or fail to work, or what may happen to them. It turned out that most of us had been taught something about vision at school, but by and large in such a way as to leave our curiosity unaroused.

After a considerable amount of time spent in reading and listening to all I conveniently could on the subject— fascinated, if at first somewhat bewildered, by the technicalities and overwhelming amount of available material— I have selected what appealed to me as the most provocative facts, and have tried to put them together in a consecutive story.

Before I enjoyed the books and articles listed in the bibliography, my ignorance about eyes was abysmal, so my deep gratitude goes to the authors and publishers of these works. I certainly do not pretend that mine is a scholarly tome, my only hope being that it may lead the reader pleasantly to greater awareness and a desire to explore further along the inspiring paths of perception.

I am impressed with the fact that the greatest thing a human soul ever does in this world is to see something, and tell what it saw in a plain way. Hundreds of people can talk for one who can see. To see clearly is poetry, philosophy, and religion all in one.

—RALPH WALDO EMERSON

Chapter 1

THE DAWN OF SENSITIVITY

A. Simple cross section of the human eye—a sphere about one inch in diameter.

1. Cornea: a curved, transparent "windowpane," the anterior one-sixth of the eyeball's protective coat.

2. Sclera: the "white" of the eye—firm, fibrous, covered by a thin, moist skin (the conjunctiva); this makes up the other five-sixths of the eyeball's coat.

3. Aqueous humor: a salty liquid which supplies nourishment to both cornea and lens, and keeps the pressure inside the eyeball at a constant level.

4. Iris: the "window shade," varying in color, pierced in the center to make an expansible and contractible pupil for full admittance or reduction of light. *(bulging on this side)*

5. Lens: a soft, crystalline, biconvex mechanism through which light entering the eye is focused on the retina.

6. Ciliary muscles: these loosen the passive pull of ligaments suspending the elastic lens, allowing it to bulge and so alter its focusing power.

7. Vitreous humor: a clear, rigid jelly which fills out the eyeball behind the lens.

8. Retina: sensory layers at the back and sides of the eyeball's inner wall, containing rods and cones which receive light focused on them by the lens.

9. Macula: a yellow, oval depression, about 3 mm. across, its central part (*fovea centralis*) being the point of acutest vision.

10. Optic disc: a circular area where all retinal layers, except the optic nerve fibers, are lacking, making it insensitive to light, therefore known as the "blind spot."

11. Optic nerve: a "cable" which conveys impulses from light patterns received by the retina to the brain for recognition, or perception.

B. Optic nerves, shown from the top, crossing on their way from the eyeballs to the brain.

C. Section showing interior of eye, with blood vessels branching on to the retina.

D. Recti muscles. These make the eyeballs turn inward, sideways, up, or down.

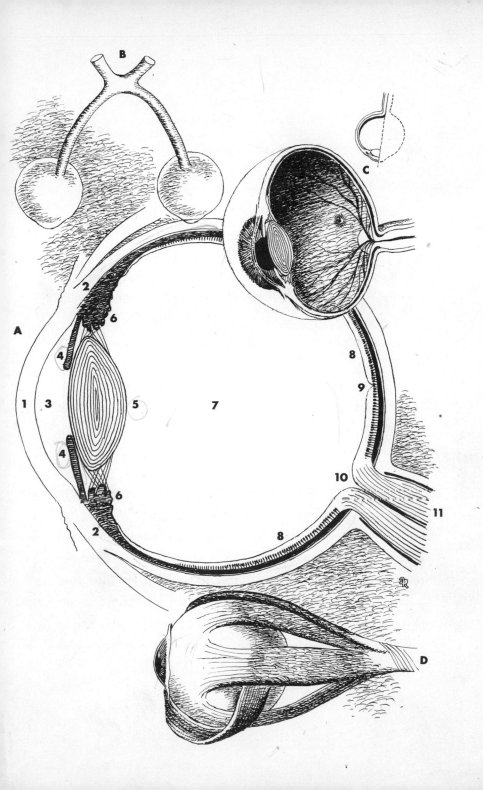

If one is sufficiently lavish with time, everything possible happens.

—Herodotus

WE *are* what we see, and most of us see only the half of it. This is not always due to laziness, neither is it necessarily because of bad eyesight or a faulty brain.

How widely animals can see—and by animals I mean all living things that move, other than the plants—depends largely upon whether the animal is all eyes, or has four eyes, or a single eye beneath his mouth or on top of his head, or two in front, or two waving about on stalks, or a whole row dotted around the edge of him.

It happens that, at the present time, human eyes are set in a pair in front of the face near the top. Although we can turn our eyes to the right or left, in order to see fully to either side we must turn our heads; and unless we turn our bodies, or use some mechanical device such as a mirror, we cannot see what goes on behind us at all. This is one of the reasons why our eyes are inferior to those of certain other animals, particularly birds. Our eyes can play tricks on us, or prove unable to register certain objects, which might well start us wondering whether or not everything is exactly as it appears to be, although in many instances, if not all, the brain is really to blame.

Over two thousand years ago, Lucretius realized that eyes are capable only of looking, and that all recognition of objects is done by the brain. "Look thou perceive," he wrote, "lest haply thou shouldst guess that the white objects shining to thine eyes are gendered of white atoms, or the black of a black seed."

If you want to try a simple example of an optical illusion, of signals misread by your brain, fix your gaze unblinkingly on some object across the room. Then stretch out your arm, with the five fingers spread slightly apart and pointing upward, until your hand comes level with the object at which you are looking, at full arm's length. Keep your gaze fixed on the object; do not look at your hand directly. Now count the number of fingers you think you see.

How much animals, including ourselves, understand, enjoy, and use what they see depends upon the kind of brain each one has, and its ability to realize, possibly improve, and finally file away for future use all that the eyes reflect and the nerve channels signal from the eyes to the brain. Eyes alone, no matter how beautiful they may seem, are as useless without a brain as a telescope in a locked drawer with the key lost. However, working healthily together and properly used, eyes and brain form one of the greatest partnerships in nature.

Which brings up a point, the understanding of which may prove useful all along the line. This is the true meaning of the words "see" and "perceive." In the introduction to his book *Language in Action* (New York: Harcourt, Brace and Company, 1941), S. I. Hayakawa writes, "There are few occasions on which Mr. Smith thinks about words as such. He wonders from time to time about a grammatical point. . . . Occasionally, too, he notices, usually with irritation, that words sometimes 'mean different things to different people.' . . . Whether he realizes it or not, however, Mr. Smith is affected every hour of his life not only by the words he hears and uses, *but also by his unconscious assumptions about language.* These unconscious assumptions determine the way he takes words— which in turn determines the way he acts, whether wisely or foolishly."

I suppose that most of us have had conversations in the course of which we have said, "Oh, I see what you mean." This is common practice, and sounds less stuffy than the more correct phrase, "Oh, I perceive your meaning." Put at its simplest, our eyes *see*—that is, they receive images of objects. It remains for our brains to *perceive*—that is, to understand, to obtain knowledge. Seeing is *looking* with the eye. Perception is *awareness*, which can be experienced by a person with a healthy brain (and senses).

Although all the senses—and, in a few cases, extra-sensory perception as well—are necessary for the complete functioning of life in a considerable number of creatures, in many instances sight is the most important, particularly to humans, because without it the distance between one object and another cannot readily be judged. This is the *basic* usefulness of the eye. The more elaborate and soul-satisfying uses to which eyes can be put—the delight which they can channel from nature and the visual arts, or from an expression on a face—belong at the other end of the story.

For the story of eyes covers vast stretches of time. It gradually reveals, through the ceaseless interplay of natural forces and conditions, our progress from the first microscopic, blind, unprotected living organisms to our present state as highly sensitive beings, capable not only of making this world a better place in which to live, but perhaps even of moving upward again into space itself—just as life, long ago, came up to dry land from the primeval sea.

The road has never been straight upward. Evolution is no steady march from the first living cell to modern man, but is full of trial and error. It is a brave struggle from mystery to mystery, a branching out and a twigging of infinite variety, and at the same time a partially defeated withering down. No great advance has been made along certain lines without a corresponding withdrawal.

When did the story begin? We do not know exactly how long it is since eyes began to look on this earth. Perhaps because of the brevity of our lives, most of us are in the habit of thinking in terms of beginning, middle, and end. Our limited minds cannot conceive the possible beginning *or no-beginning*, the end *or no-end* of the cosmos. In fact, it is not easy for us to comprehend the possible age of even our own planet—so enormous a stretch of time that within it the length of *human* existence, from primitive to present-day man, is like the thinness of a sheet of tissue paper compared to the height of the tallest skyscraper.

In the "beginning"—to take the word in its Biblical sense —in the beginning, the world was probably without oceans. At that time, the terrific heat of the earth possibly dried up all moisture, driving it upward into thick layers of steam clouds which perpetually blotted out the light of the sun. During that black chaos of birth, and for ages afterward, the earth bubbled and heaved mightily, spinning and flaming in an eternal night, while great cyclonic storms screamed and tore over its surface. It is more than likely that in time, as the earth cooled, the clouds liquefied and fell in interminable rains, flooding the wrinkles and chasms and huge cups of the hardening earth to form vast warm seas.

As the rains fell and the sea increased, so that the entire world was covered by it, the layers of cloud thinned until at last they opened and let through a pale, watery sunshine. Light, the source of sight, had penetrated to earth.

At some time in those dim millenniums, life began. Today scientists, in their never-ending search for origins, incline to the theory that the first life was produced, in that huge hothouse of the new-made world, by an exact complementing of temperature, chemicals, and pressures at the right time in the slight saltiness of the primeval sea. Life may have originated in the undersea rocks, as minute specks of chemical activity, so simply constructed that they fed directly upon inorganic food like that which nourishes certain bacteria today. Later, when the earth's atmosphere became purified of its noxious gases and the sea of certain acids, a more advanced form of life became possible—bacteria, the first known microorganisms to exist outside the rocks. Between the two—between the active, nonliving chemical specks (in the sense, generally accepted up to now, that chemicals are nonliving) and the living bacteria —there seems to have been a "missing link." This link has possibly been identified recently by two scientists.

Viruses may occupy the twilight between the living and the "nonliving." These infinitesimal agents, capable of causing a number of diseases in animals and plants, have long puzzled biologists. Some consider them to be true living organisms. Others believe that they are just complex proteins and nucleic acids, substances basic to life, but in viruses able to multiply only as parasites in living cells. (The present general definition of life is anything that grows *and perpetuates itself or its species*.) In June 1955, two scientists (Drs. Heinz L. Fraenkal-Conrad and Robley Williams, of the University of California Virus Laboratory, of which Dr. Wendell M. Stanley, Nobel Laureate, is head) were studying the virus of mosaic disease, which causes frightful damage to tobacco plants. To tobacco growers this virus, which divides the leaves sharply into light and dark green patches, seems to behave like any other disease-producing live organism, but when biologists isolate the virus in their test tubes they find it to be nothing but a regular crystal-forming molecule, rather like ordinary salt—an apparently lifeless chemical.

The two professors claimed that they had killed the virus, put the dead parts together again, and restored complete reactivity. They added, however, that it might take several years before they could make the newly alive virus reproduce itself in the test tube.

This opens the exciting possibility that some day the raw materials of life may be created in the laboratory out of what we have been calling "lifeless" chemicals, perhaps giving us a clue to the intermediate stage between those primitive chemical specks, at the dawn of the world, and the first bacteria.

The next living things of importance to our story are the algae, ancestors of the seaweeds, important because of their reaction to light. Spreading in blue-green masses near the surface of the warm primordial sea, the algae were plants without distinct roots, stems, or leaves—thin branching threads sheathed in a slippery mucilage.

Algae, like all green plants after them, build up requirements for their existence—carbohydrates—by a process called photosynthesis. The plant cells absorb carbon dioxide from the air, and under the action of sunlight on the colored pigments in the plant (green chlorophyll, yellow carotene, and yellow xantophyll) the carbon dioxide and some of the water in the plant cells are converted into carbohydrates and oxygen. We know that the pigments absorb the radiant energy, but we are not yet certain as to the details of photosynthesis.

All these processes took millions of years to develop, during which the division of living things into plants and animals probably took place. The earliest animals known to us are called protozoa. Most of these consist of a single cell, as do plants like the bacteria, and they reproduce by means of fission—that is, by dividing themselves into two or more parts, each of which is a complete new organism.

A cell is a small, usually microscopic mass of protoplasm surrounded by a semi-permeable, skinlike surface. It generally includes a nucleus, a specialized portion of great importance to life, particularly to heredity. The word protoplasm comes from the Greek, and means "the first thing formed." Protoplasm is a colloid, which is another word of Greek derivation meaning "like glue," a fluid, diffusible, noncrystallizable substance, the basic elements of which are carbon, hydrogen, oxygen, and nitrogen. These elements are made up of atoms, and atoms are made of protons, neutrons, and electrons, so that a colloid may be said to consist of the same material as the planets.

From bacteria to the stars—that is the astonishing span of the story of eyes, for it will grow from the original, light-sensitive living things right through to what may happen to the eyes of man as he launches on his journey into inter-planetary space.

So, simply as laymen, we might now stop taking our eyes for granted, and begin to inquire about them with curiosity. All through the ages, in adjusting for life under difficult, changing conditions, nature has often given top priority to the eyes of those who used best what they had. Nothing that may happen to eyes in the future could be much more astounding than what has happened to them in the tremendous past.

The story unfolds in strange, slow steps, full of wonderment. It opens with a mere primitive sensation, a turning toward the light, as leaves and flowers turn, like the quiet beginnings of a dance.

Chapter 2

SIGHT IN THE SEA

The simplest of all specialized eyes first appeared in a creature probably very like the much enlarged Euglena seen here, lashing its whiplike flagellum into a ray of light. There are many markings resembling eyes on its body—particularly the spotted circle within a circle near the tail, which is the nucleus—but the actual sensitive eyespot is the black patch near the base of the flagellum, just above the circle surrounded by eight smaller ones. Under a microscope the eye is seen to be a rose-colored boss made up of six small spots, or lenses.

The scallop, below, is opening its shell in order to swim, thus exposing its double row of green eyespots. These are more complicated than the euglena's primitive spot, each one being in itself as true an eye as any to be found in animals without a backbone.

THE SEA lay everywhere.

Somewhere, just below the surface in the warm, filtered green sunshine, a microscopic, single-celled creature swayed with the waters. It floated in a beautiful forest of threadlike algae, from which it was not far removed in structure, but of which it was totally unaware except when heavier patches masked the light.

This speck of life belonged to the group known as Flagellata, of the phylum Protozoa, which are generally supposed to be the first form of animal life to appear on our world. The flagellata possessed certain parts called organelles, among them being a mouth aperture and a refractive globule, or so-called eyespot. It is likely, however, that not only this eyespot but the entire body was sensitive to light, although all that it "saw" was a patternless glow from above; it had a sensitivity (heliotropism, a turning toward or away from light) like that of the early plants. Such sensitivity to light was not real sight, but might be termed a first step toward it, showing that light falling on a living thing could make it *do* something.

The power of moving from one place to another—stimulated primarily by the need to hunt for food beyond the areas where it might be obtained simply by opening a mouth aperture and sucking in—this power possibly developed with the various senses, particularly that of vision, which is essential to the *immediate* judgment of distance between one object and another. So when that small flagellata sensed a shadow passing across it, it took for granted, perhaps rashly, that it was food, for that was all it knew. Quickly it began to beat a whiplike thread, or flagellum, in front of it in consecutive half-circles, pushing the water backward and lashing itself forward. It progressed slowly but with astonishing persistence, making several trials and errors before it finally hit upon the right path and came to its prey. This it proceeded to ingest with equal patience. Flagellata had all the time in the world.

The hard-won morsel was not easy to ingest—it was an encysted Euglena, a minute, protoplasmic life form prob ably very like the unknown animal in which the eye first definitely appeared as a separate organ rather than as an entire light-sensitive surface.

Nobody has yet been able to determine whether the euglena is a plant or an animal. It seems to occupy that no man's land between the two forms of life, much as the tobacco-disease virus seems to lie between the living and the nonliving. Plants may be said to have a kind of "instinct," although very little compared to that of even the lowest animals. This primordial behavior in plants was very possibly the beginning of those trials and reactions which were to direct the trend of evolution *within the limit of its environment.*

A vitally important step onward in the evolution of animal life was a protective covering. This at first was probably very like the cell it protected, but as time went on it changed considerably. For one thing, it acquired pigmentation, possibly a dark brown coloration, the purpose of which was probably to prevent undue loss of the radiant energy which it acquired from sunlight, and also to protect it from undue exposure to "sunburn" (ultraviolet light). After much more time had gone by, this pigmentation finally settled in one spot, which became particularly sensitive to light. This "eyespot" was capable of sensing not only the light but also the direction from which it came, when one side of the spot was more brilliantly illuminated than the other. If the spot happened to be sufficiently large, shadows falling upon it might convey a definite pattern, but there was no sense of detail, and the animal could experience nothing of any object that was too far away to throw a shadow over the sensitive spot, because the spot contained no mechanism with which to focus the light from the distant thing.

Around the speck of pigment were the microscopic

flagella as in many of the earlier, single-celled creatures, although now there were many more of them, and their name has been changed from flagella to cilia, meaning eyelash. However, these must not be thought of in the same sense as our eyelashes, because the primitive creatures of the sea needed no rest-giving eyelids, no screening lashes or cleansing tears, for as yet their sight organs were far from being true eyes, and the gentle wash of the sea over them was all that was needed to keep them free from irritation.

The specialized eye of the euglena—the simplest of all specialized eyes—appeared as a tiny rose-colored boss set just below the mouth. Under a strong microscope, this boss can be seen to be made up of six small spots, or lenses. But at first the euglena's eye was not much of a success. It could never take in the full picture of the strange, growing sea world around it, although it did act as a sort of compass and thermometer, sensing the direction and intensity of light and heat. It was capable of vaguely registering form and movement, but there was one great drawback— it was constantly being injured, because it stood out beyond the surface of the skin. However, as the centuries passed, the eyes of some euglenas grew less prominent, and in time the rosy little boss of magical pigment became habitually set in a cuplike depression.

Some five hundred million years ago, the algae had increased the number of their cells and grown larger and

stronger, more like our present-day seaweeds, in prepara-
tion for their eventual invasion of dry land. The protozoa
had advanced into the unicelled, delicately beautiful
Foraminifera and Radiolaria, and among the now teeming
multitude of weird and lovely multicellular creatures appeared stony corals and sea anemones, starfishes (with an
eyespot at the end of each ray), sea urchins, paddling
bells, snails, mosslike Bryozoa, nautilus, squids, octopuses,
and joint-limbed denizens of the rocky sea bottom herald-
ing the shrimps, lobsters, crabs, scorpions, cockroaches,
and all insects.

All these creatures were invertebrates. None of them
had backbones, in the sense understood by us, as their
name implies. The skins of the joint-limbed animals were
hard, forming an *exterior* skeleton which protected and
held together the body—but it should be noted that the
word "skeleton" does not necessarily include a backbone.
Many of them had developed legs, an equal number on
each side of their bodies, which simplified locomotion and
the capture of food on and around the rocks; also "arms"
or pincers with which to seize their prey, and eyes on the
end of little stalks. These took thousands of centuries to
develop, as did all the changes taking place in the dwellers
of the sea.

In the story of sight, the cephalopods are especially
strange and wonderful—the nautilus, squids, octopuses,
and others similarly constructed. Paired eyes, which we

usually think of as a normal arrangement, perhaps because
we ourselves possess two, now appeared in these creatures,
symmetrically placed one on each side of the upper surface of the head. The purpose of paired eyes was to give
the animal a means of orienting himself in reference to
his own longitudinal midplane and to the surface of the
ocean.

The eyes of nautilus are among the most curious features of this remarkable animal. Placed on the head, which
springs directly from the enormous foot, the eyes are
slightly projecting boxes, like little kettledrums, about half
an inch in diameter. In the center of each drum is a pinhole, through which the light falls upon the sunken spot
of sensitive pigment, to make a picture much as occurs in
a pinhole camera. The sea continually washes gently in
and out of this almost microscopic aperture to keep the
eye fresh and clean.

In other cephalopods the pinhole in the thin covering of
the eyespot closed up entirely, but, in order to admit light,
remained transparent. This minute skin "hole stopper"
thickened, in the course of time, and curved slightly to
form a primitive lens, which could bend and focus the
light rays into a somewhat more exact picture on the light-
sensitive cells inside.

Now came the most remarkable additions of all, pre-
cursors of parts of our own eyes. Those sensitive cells
which were around the primitive pigment spot in early

forms of life gradually built up, in these later forms, to make what are known as iridian folds (from Iris, goddess of the rainbow), near the axis of the eye; then they continued upward to the skin surface to grow into an outer, circular little wall around the lens. This wall bent over to cover the lens completely with a transparent skin, and became the cornea or "windowpane" of the developing eye. The iridian folds, or iris, had a free, circular inner margin which could be puckered up by a ringlike muscle called the sphincter. The iris acts as a thin partition, or diaphragm, between the cornea and the focusing lens, a sort of window shade which gathers up in a circular manner to make a small central opening when the light is bright, and a larger one when it is dim.

This variable opening is the pupil, named from the Latin word *pupilla,* meaning "little girl." The rather odd name was chosen to describe the miniature reflection, in the eye, of the person at which it is looking, although that reflection is really on the "windowpane" cornea, and not on the pupil. A surprisingly large number of people are still unaware that the pupils of their eyes are actually nothing but *holes* in the iris, leading to the dark interior, and are *not* solid black matter that dilates and contracts.

At the same time that the sea washed over the surface of these primitive, lidless eyes, keeping them clear and clean, it also permeated and lubricated the interior by osmosis. The sea also served to plump out the eyes, which otherwise would have been just layers of papery tissue.

As amazing as their wonderful eyes are the various ways in which deep-water cephalopods provide themselves with light by which to see or attract their food, far down where all trace of sunlight has been filtered out. Excitement of any kind, including response to the colors of surrounding objects, will affect the color of shallow-water species, but among deep-water squid blazing displays of phosphorescent color occur. Some of these squid, brought up from great depths and kept alive in chilled water, have had their photographs taken by their own light. They are adorned with diadems of gleaming color; their eyes shine with a deep blue light, or sometimes with a pearly sheen. Other organs on the lower surfaces of their bodies add to the thrilling effect with a ruby light. Some squid possess a sort of bull's-eye lantern, others have mirrored searchlights, while yet others throw out a luminous secretion which flows behind them in long, silver-beaded threads. But there are fish living in the darkest ocean depths who do not even try to see their way about. They have allowed their eyes to atrophy—thrown them away, as it were—and rely upon the development of a general intense sensitivity by which to avoid their enemies and find food in the perpetual night of their environment.

Of great importance among the new life appearing in the sea were the curious types known as brachiopods and trilobites. The brachiopods were complex marine animals, bearing a resemblance, purely superficial, to clams. The now extinct trilobites looked not unlike our present-day horseshoe or king crabs, which, however, are arachnids.

None of these creatures of the early seas had a true reasoning brain, but in a sense clams and oysters, for example, may be termed "brainy." The three pairs of "brains" of their somewhat complicated nervous systems are swellings, or ganglia, of the larger nerves. One pair of these ganglia controls the action parts of the mantle (the folds of the body wall which line and secrete the edge of the shell) and the mouth. They also receive messages from the minute organs of balance, the octocysts, which become related to ears in further-developed animals. The second pair of major ganglia activates the foot—large in clams, which use their feet for digging, and smaller in oysters, which do not use feet. The third pair are the visceral ganglia. In scallops, these visceral ganglia are connected with their eyes, a neat necklace of emerald-green spots set around the edge of the mantle.

True paired eyes are found in the larvae of many bivalves, but they are always lost when the adult stage is reached. Adult clams and mussels have developed pigment spots sensitive only to changing light, but each tiny eye in the scallop's emerald chain is as true an eye as any to be found in animals without a backbone. Each is equipped with a cornea (that "horny," transparent, protective windowpane), a focusing lens, a retina at the base of the eye to receive the focused images, and a connecting nerve leading to the ganglia—an eye of intricate parts, each of which evolved, over huge stretches of time, in its own peculiar way. When the scallop moves, it can look where it is going, because it propels itself by opening and shutting the two parts of its shell and "biting" into the water ahead, thus exposing its eyes.

The eyes of oysters, although they do not possess any of the highly developed parts found in scallops' eyes, nevertheless are extraordinarily sensitive, and show that sometimes the sense of sight can be superior to other senses. At the very instant that the shadow of an enemy falls across its tiny eyespots, the oyster immediately snaps its shell shut with astonishing speed, well before the disturbance of the water could warn it of danger through its sense of touch. This shell-shutting, however, is a purely reflex action, simply the result of a nervous impulse transmitted inward from its eyespots to the ganglia and outward again to the muscles controlling the shell, for the oyster has nothing like a brain which can reason.

Although the primitive animals had no true brain, it would seem that at times they did have a kind of memory. They repeated actions which they had proved, after countless trials and errors, to be successful. Certainly they reacted to light and other stimulation through the eye, if only in a reflex manner. This has been proved by an interesting experiment on the king crab.

The king crab has four eyes, set in the upper side of its arched, chitinous head shield. Two are placed close together, near the center, each with a single lens looking fixedly upward toward the light above the ocean. The other two eyes are situated one on each side of the shell, immovably directed to right and left into the light planes in which the crab moves. These two lateral eyes are compound—that is, they are made up of several lenses, the forerunners of insect eyes. The single-lensed, simple eyes directed upward can distinguish little more than light and shade, but the compound side eyes reflect the form and movement of objects. When a small electric current passes through a nerve connected to a muscle, the muscle contracts. A single nerve fiber was separated from the optic nerve of a king crab, and electrodes were attached to it. A light shone on the eye created a regular sequence of uniform electrical charges which traveled along the nerve. As the eye was further stimulated by increasing the strength of the light, the frequency of the electrical charges also increased, showing the direct relation of light to conduction of impulses along the optic nerve.

A lavish amount of time passed by in the continuance of the journey of eyes from primitive pigment spots to near perfection, during which the first vertebrates came into being—backboned and brain-bearing fishes, in whose eyes our own had their real beginning.

Chapter 3

BACKBONES AND BRAINS

The beginnings of a nervous system and brain, without which eyes are useless, appeared in such animals as the lancelet, or amphioxus, a cross section of which is given at the bottom of the illustration opposite. The segmented notochord, or rudimentary backbone, can be seen stretching from end to end of its body. Above the notochord is the neurochord, containing the nervous system, which broadens at the head into a brain cavity in which the eyespot is situated.

Immediately above the amphioxus is a lamprey, related to those inhabitants of both salt and fresh water the fossils of which give us the first records of primitive backbones. The eyes of lampreys are clearly defined, one on each side of the head. The earliest true vertebrates, however, were sea fish such as the shark shown here above the lamprey. The skeleton at the top is that of a swordfish, revealing the well-formed backbone.

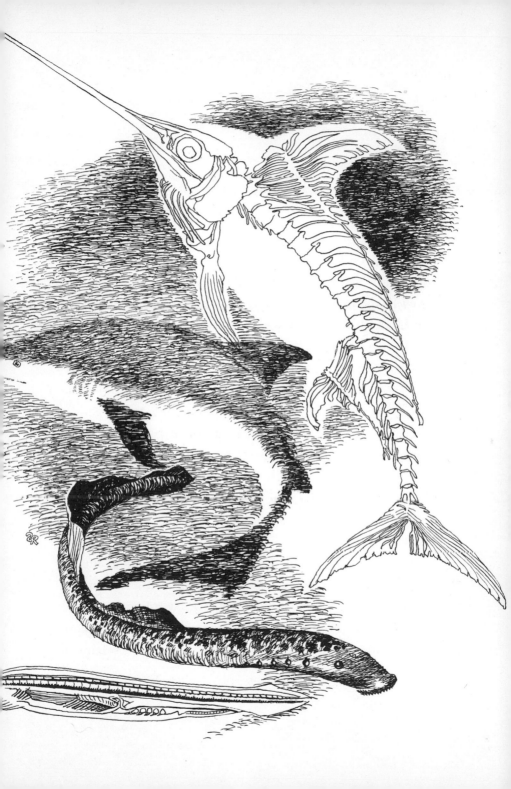

*Nature drives with a loose rein, and vitality of
any sort . . . can blunder through many a pre-
dicament in which reason would despair.*
—George Santayana, *The Sense of Beauty*

A QUARTER of the world's surface had risen above
the sea, perhaps not for the first time. Between the
rocky sand dunes of the new land lay quiet, stagnant pools
of brackish water, thick with algae.

Two great changes in life were taking place.

The first sea creatures had obtained oxygen, necessary
for their existence, by a simple chemical process. Now they
were learning to use a new, more complicated apparatus
that had evolved in the long course of time—gills. They
began to breathe their oxygen from the water through
these slits, or gills, which would slowly develop into lungs
capable of breathing the atmosphere on dry land.

By this time, many of the earliest forms of sea life were
already fading out in the struggle for adaptation to changing conditions, while others had reached their highest
possible peak of evolution. Among the latter was a now
extinct group of arachnids—gigantic scorpions, some of
them about three feet in length. Two of these scorpions,
Paleophonus and *Proscorpius*, left the sea, perhaps in

search of more easily obtainable food—and so it was that
life first came up on dry land.

The second great change arrived through the advent of
what are known as chordates, in the first rivers of that time.

Since the "beginning," the surface of the earth had been
constantly changing. It heaved, cracked, rose into huge
mountains or fell into abysmal chasms. Vast wind and rain
storms tore at the rocks, grinding them into powder, and
periods of bitter cold cracked and crumbled them away.
Whole chains of mountains wore away completely, and
continents sank under the weight of their debris, so that
the seas crept over them again, stayed for further ages,
then once more receded, leaving in the brackish pools
on land many primitive, living sea creatures. Rain-water
lakes, formed in the high hollows of new-born mountains,
flooded and raced to the sea as rivers, eddying into the
brackish pools. The rivers carried with them many minerals from the rocks at their source and along their beds,
including calcium, which was to be vital in the food of the
coming bony animals.

In these fresh-water rivers, not far from the sea coasts,
there lived strange little animals, seemingly headless, jaw-
less, their blood colorless as water, and their bodies pointed
at both ends. These animals were possibly rather like the
present-day lancelet, or amphioxus, which means "double-
pointed." They belonged to the phylum of chordates—
"having a chord"—and were about three inches long, semi-

transparent, with a lovely play of iridescent color about them.

A lazy, little-moving form of lancelet exists in the sea today. From it we can make a probably pretty close guess as to the structure of primitive lancelets. It is formed symmetrically, equal on both sides, with a segmented body, gill slits, and a cord running down its back, protected by a thick membrane that also serves to stiffen and hold together the segments of its body. The body is divided into four parts: head, upper body, abdominal section, and tail—although at first it is difficult to tell head from tail.

The notochord, as the cord along its back is called, extends to the extreme tip at both ends of its body. It is an elastic cord, extremely important in our story, because, in the first lancelets or their like, it provided the basis for all segmented backbones in later vertebrates, from fish to man.

Immediately above the notochord lies another cylindrical cord, also surrounded by a sheath of connecting tissues, called the neurochord, from the Greek *neuron,* meaning "a nerve." This cord is made up of those nerve fibers already seen in the first sea creatures. It is neither elastic nor solid, and it surrounds a small central canal which is the nervous system of the lancelet, containing the beginnings of what would become the brain and spinal marrow in the higher forms of life, including our own.

In the head of the little animal, the neurochord broadens

out into a thin-walled brain cavity, in the front part of which is a collection of dark-pigmented cells making up an eyespot, visible through the transparent skin, but not sensitive to light. In addition to the cerebral eyespot there are numbers of minute black-pigmented spots beside and below the central canal of the neurochord, which are of the nature of eyes, sometimes called the spinal eyes, and which are light-sensitive. Over the cerebral eyespot is a small "nose," known to biologists as von Kölliker's olfactory pit.

The first definite records we have of true backbones (in contrast to simple cords) are in fossils of fishes related to the modern lamprey, eel-like inhabitants of both salt and fresh water. The bodies of these first vertebrates were designed for speed in swimming, so essential for escape from enemies and for the trapping of food, in the increasingly dense population of the early sea. Lampreys, like lancelets, did not leave the safety of their rivers for the sea until they had completely mastered control of locomotion and simultaneous defense.

The lamprey has two moderate-sized eyes, one on each side of the head, which reflect impressions for the brain. As in all fishes, the brain is smooth, narrow, and elongated, capable of recognizing pictures of surrounding objects sent to it from the eyes by the connecting nerves, but because of its simple form unable to *think* about what it sees.

Perhaps the most curious thing about lampreys is a peculiar eyelike apparatus growing out of the top of the brain, from a double projection called the pineal. In the early forms of this animal, the projections dilated to become a cavity, its deep lower part forming a "retina," its upper wall being clear and translucent, like a lens. The retinal section is packed tightly with an opaque white pigment, some of which also fills the lens section. Although this looks like a third, middle eye, complete with white "eyeball," it is thought by some to have been not an eye at all, but a thermometer, registering only heat and cold.

It is a known fact that vertebrates have already lost an eye, although whether they lost it before or after reaching the vertebrate stage is not certain, and anyway probably all it could do was register light. No three-eyed vertebrate fossil has been found so far, but in fossils of some early reptiles the vestige of a third eye is seen, connected to the site of the pineal gland. The reason for the existence of this gland remains somewhat of a mystery. Descartes declared that it was the seat of the soul, attached to a functioning "window." In the ascent of the animal scale, it becomes less and less noticeable, until in the higher vertebrates, ourselves included, it is no more than a buried glandular structure, an apparently useless remnant.

When the primitive vertebrates left the rivers for the sea, they entered surroundings which were intensely beautiful and varied. Delicate corals towered in the now more

salty water, between them forests of tall, swaying seaweeds, intricately fronded and laden with fruitlike pods.
Smaller, algal seaweeds grew in the blue-green sunshine
near the surface, while the dark, rocky caverns glowed
with the colored lights of deep-water creatures, and starfish hung in great galaxies, over a mile long, above beds of
edible mussels. A snow of little white dead shells, constantly falling, made a carpet for the sea.

For about one hundred million years, the fishes that had
entered the sea from the rivers increased and took on a
variety of forms, until they completely overran the invertebrates there. Today, about five hundred million years
since their origin, they still form the largest class of all
vertebrates, outnumbered among living things only by
the insects.

The first true vertebrates in the sea were sharklike in
form. They lived in the surface waters, where they could
reap the most benefit from the radiant energy of sunlight.
Water absorbs ultraviolet and infrared light, but contains
a small portion of the entire spectrum of radiant energy.
Visible light, however, disappears rather rapidly in the sea
as the depth increases, and is entirely lost at about two
thousand feet.

Fishes have no necks, which is one reason why their eyes
are arranged so that they can see almost all around themselves without turning their bodies. There are a few
armored types with movable scales to allow the head to

bend up and down, however. Fishes have four "limbs," paired fins which they use in locomotion, and which became increasingly important as their advance up to the land approached.

The skeletons of the early sharklike fishes were built of cartilage, and imbedded in their skin were small pieces of enamel, like the coating of their teeth. One of the first sharks known to us had a well-developed vertebral column, and a levered lower jaw attached to the brain case by two articulations—one immediately behind the eye and one at the back of the skull.

The brain case, shaped like a trough, protected the brain from below and from the sides, but not completely from above, as in most other vertebrates. (In forms with a bony skeleton, such as the shark's ancestors are thought to have possessed, there was a dermal roof overhead, doing away with the need for a complete brain case.) Far forward, in the orbital region, the brain case of the sharklike fishes narrowed to aid in forming a socket, the orbit, for the eyeball and its muscles. Protected by this brain case, the nerve cells, or "brain," began to grow, possibly stimulated by the increasingly complicated environment of the sea, which called for greater awareness and swifter reaction.

The sense of sight was now becoming more and more allied with the other senses; it was considerably furthered by the senses of smell and touch, and particularly by sound. In the first vertebrate fishes, the sense of touch concentrated into one particular organ known as the labyrinth, which was more suited to their watery environment. The labyrinth was a small closed sac, partly filled with water, and had a dual purpose—it was somewhat like a telephone receiver, collecting sounds, and at the same time was a spirit level, registering the fish's position in space, or balance.

From these collected sensations—sight, locomotion, smell, touch, hearing, and balance—came consciousness, which later was to develop into mind. In time, the nerve cells connected with the source of each of these senses increased in quantity, efficiency, and coordination one with another. Being situated close together, they gradually became one controlling organ, the brain, capable of exercising memory and, later, anticipation, from which arose instinct.

This new, astounding mechanism was made up of three parts, according to the position of each particular nerve cell in relation to the sense organ to which it was attached: the forebrain, principally concerned with smell, the nasal openings being at the front end of the skull, or snout; the midbrain, connected with vision and also with correlated locomotive control; and the hindbrain, which contained the labyrinth, controlling balance.

As brainpower increased, so did the possibilities of vision. The great duet between eyes and brain began.

The brain wall originated in a very queer way. It started with the sinking of a large area of skin into the head. On this skin were the little primitive eyespots, and in the sinking they became twisted about and buried. Because the sunshine in which the first vertebrate fishes lived had darkened the pigmentation of their skin, and because new layers of tissue had grown, the buried eyespots were completely cut off from light—blinded. As a remedy for this, the sinking of the eyespots was reversed, so that they outpocketed from the brain wall, of which they had become a part, and again came up, like small bubbles, to their functional position under the skin of the "face." At that particular place the skin was thin and transparent, and, as it had done with the invertebrates, it sank into the little clump of outpocketed cells and made a lens for the focusing of light rays. Consequently, the vertebrate eye is in two parts: a cerebral (brain) part, which is the retina, and an epithelial (skin) part, which is the lens and its transparent covering, the cornea.

Some of the light-sensitive skin which had sunk in to form part of the brain wall, and which was not needed for the eyebuds, remained inside the nervous system and lost much of its sensitivity, but there are still patches of "visual" tissue in even the highest forms of vertebrate animals, located mostly in the midbrain. These patches receive a faint illumination, although the light must penetrate through the entire side of the head.

Because it had been buried and twisted about, the vertebrate eyespot, or retina—that sensitive net at the base of the eye which traps images focused by the lens, sending them through the optic nerve to the brain—was inside out. It remains so to this day, our own included. The little sensitive hairs on it, which from the first one-celled living creature had always faced outward toward the light, now pointed away from it toward the back of the eye. Strangely enough, this made little difference to the formation of clear pictures, because the nerve cells and fibers overlaying these cilia, between them and the light, were thin and transparent.

It is important for detailed pictures that the cilia be set close together, like the pile on fine velvet. This does not happen in animals of poor eyesight, but we ourselves have approximately one hundred and thirty-two million of them in each eye; birds have many more, and in some deep-sea fishes there are twenty-five million of them to the square millimeter. However, these fishes' cells are more sensitive to light than to form.

Obviously, the finer the light-sensitive hairs are, and the closer they are set together, the better the pictures they receive. The first vertebrate-fish retinal cells were fine, but not the finest known by a long way, and they could not see in great detail. Their world was rather like a picture newspaper—black, gray, and white, with the clarity depending upon the number of cilia and on how thickly these were placed together, much as the clarity of certain printed pictures depends upon the number of little dots upon the plate, the only difference being that the fish were aware that some of their pictures moved.

Generally speaking, the eyes of early vertebrate fishes were much alike, and have remained the same ever since. The eyeball is not quite spherical, but slightly flattened front and back. The lens, however, is a perfect little crystal ball. The reason for this is that the lens has to provide all the power for focusing the light, because the flattish cornea is incapable of assisting, as it does in higher forms of life, when it is more rounded. Light is focused by refraction, or "bending" of the rays of light to a certain point. Water refracts light. Since the optical density of the fish's cornea and of the water through which it looks is about the same, the cornea cannot bend the light rays farther.

In order to take in as wide a visual field as possible, the lens has to protrude through the pupil of the iris, which partly accounts for the staring look of fish. The iris has no sphincter muscle, so that the pupil always remains the same size. The iris is often beautifully colored—red, mauve, silver, gold, or green—and the effect is heightened in some fishes by a jet-black layer of pigment outside the retina, or by shining cells there, which are probably helpful in reflecting and increasing the dim light of deeper waters.

Above the retina is a layer of blood vessels (the choroid), which supply it with food and oxygen and remove waste products. The choroid is covered with a tough layer of transparent fiber (the sclera), which holds the shape of the eye and protects the delicate retina.

The eyes of most flat, side-swimming fishes are very odd. The young flounder, for instance, has eyes set in the usual manner, one on each side of its head, but as it grows older, swimming along the sea bottom and scraping the side of its head along the sand, its skull gradually becomes twisted until both eyes lie on the same side of its head, the upper. In another species, the shifting eye actually passes straight through the skull until it comes to rest in the same socket as the other eye.

Fishes can move their lens toward or away from the retina to "accommodate" the eye to the object seen, so that the picture will not be too blurred. This action of accommodation has nothing to do with the *awareness* of distance, which is worked out by the brain. Fish brains are very simple, so it remains controversial whether or not they are aware of depth in their visual field.

There are many ways among vertebrates for this focusing, or accommodation, to be arranged. Usually a small muscle directly attached to the lens pulls it back and forth. The ray, however, tilts the whole of its retinal surface in relation to the lens and front of the eye, so that it can focus nearby objects on one part of the retina and, at the same time, distant objects on another part, and has then only to move the rest of its eye to see either object clearly.

A fish which is not flat cannot look at anything with both eyes at once, because its eyes are usually set on each side of its face, back to back. Such a fish, therefore, could not see in three dimensions, as we learn to do, even if its brain were sufficiently advanced to recognize solidity in objects, which it is not. However, to make up for this, it can see a wide panorama stretching almost to the back of its head, although it does not see very clearly and, in most species, sees with little perspective.

Because it has no eyelids, a fish sees the entire picture around it unceasingly, from which the question arises whether or not fish sleep. Their attention does flag now and then, which has much the same effect as sleep. We rest our eyes a little every time we blink, but most fish, being lidless, cannot do this. In a few of the later species, there are fixed folds of skin resembling lids above and below the eyes, and some sharks have an eyelid at the inner corner of the eye which moves sideways, by contraction of its muscles, back and forth across the eyeball; but complete eyelids, as we know them, did not exist among the early creatures of the sea.

To rest their eyes, therefore, fish developed "motion blindness," which is the inability to perceive objects while the eye is moving; so that when a fish apparently turns its eye to look you over it is really seeing nothing at all.

To begin with, this important step in the development of the eye—mobility—was not necessary to *aim* the eye at an object, because any part of the early fish's retina could reflect equally well, whereas in our eyes certain parts reflect better than others. Mobility was necessary to keep objects seen from seeming to be in constant motion when they were not. If the fish's eyes had remained stationary, fixed, as in the more primitive forms, its simple brain would have been made dizzy and bewildered when it swam, or rested buffeted by the currents, because the rocks and other static matter would appear to refuse to "stay put." We ourselves, when we shake our heads, would become unpleasantly nauseated if our eyes were not free to turn in the opposite direction to each shake.

So the fish developed new muscles, the original actions of which were all reflex, to make the eyes movable and balanced in their sockets, with somewhat the action of gyroscopes. The head skin around the cornea folded in to make what is known as the conjunctiva, whose flexibility permits the eyeball to turn easily.

Fishes, like reptiles, have no maximum size, and continue to grow as long as they live, but when the eyes of early vertebrate fishes reached that stage of development most suitable to their needs they stopped growing, and have remained basically the same size ever since.

Not all fish eyes, however, evolved in equal degree. The surface fish had quite good eyes, for use in well-illuminated water. As the layers of water in which different fish lived became deeper and deeper, the eyes grew larger, with increasingly large pupils to let in what little light there was. These eyes were often placed on top of the head, as the light came from above instead of on all sides. In the deepest parts of the sea, where there was no light beyond that thrown out by phosphorescent "extra" eyes, which some fish grew to aid their "seeing" eyes, and the light given out from the bodies of other types, eyes became enormous, with highly sensitive retinas. Finally, in the completely dark caverns of the rocks, where no phosphorescent creatures existed to give off even a faint glow, eyes became mere rudiments, and sometimes disappeared entirely.

During the millions of years it took to reach these stages of development, an important change gradually appeared in the skeletons of a particular group of fish called the teleosteans, among which are tuna, herring, cod, swordfish, salmon, and pike. The first shark skeletons were made of semi-transparent, elastic cartilage, but now, with more calcium added to their food among the other important minerals brought by the rivers to the sea, the teleosteans' skeletons grew stronger, until the cartilage became bone. This, although not the first time bone had appeared (the ostracoderms, which were present in the sea before the cartilagenous fishes, possessed true bone), was invaluable in the vertebrates' eternal struggle for survival and progress.

There was yet another great contribution some of the

teleosteans were to give to life, a gift that was eventually to make possible the enjoyment of countless new habits, comforts, and beauties among the higher animals, particularly human beings.

This new wonder was a sense of color.

Chapter 4

IN FULL COLOR

A beam of white light passes through a prism, which bends and splits it into the seven colors humans see in the rainbow. This varicolored light is shown entering a man's eye, to be received by the light-sensitive retina and "telegraphed" along the optic nerve for recognition by the brain.

Behind the diagram of the human eye is a highly magnified section of a retina, with thin black areas depicting the rods, which respond mostly to night or dim light, and thicker black areas, the cones—shaped as their name implies—which react to daylight and stimulate the perception of color by the brain.

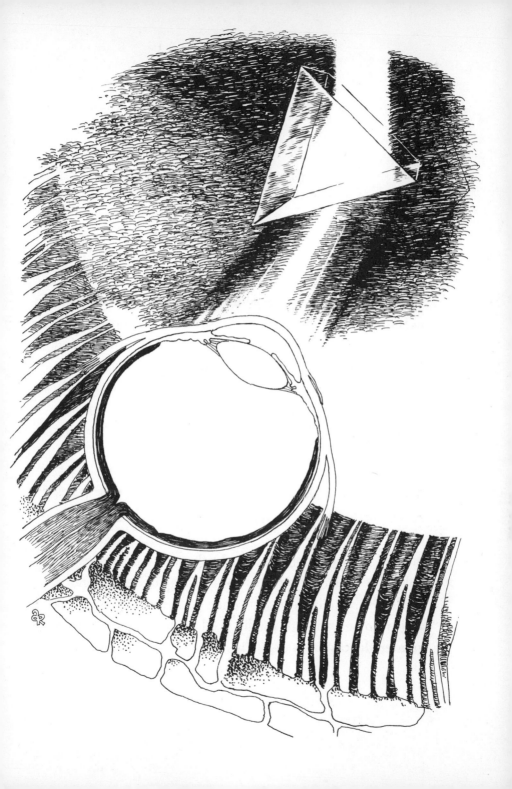

Light is the first of painters.
—Ralph Waldo Emerson, *Nature*

IT WAS a calm night, nearing its end. Rain fell quietly in a fine, silvery curtain about the gray-black rocks and water.

A little way down in the gently heaving sea, a fish rested, as though suspended by a thread from the full moon which now and then appeared between clouds. The fish seemed to stare through the rippling water at the light above, fascinated, hypnotized by the glinting surface, that deadly but beautiful barrier beyond which it could never pass alive. The night, the sea, the fish, all seemed awaiting a miracle.

Now the moon was quite clear of clouds, and there suddenly appeared above the rainswept sea a perfect arc of seven shades, silver, gray, and darker grays, like a soft chiffon scarf in the sky—a lunar rainbow. Its ghostly tints merged with the colorless world the still fish saw, while below the dark rim of the sea the sun prepared a new glory.

The fish, a teleostean, was enjoying a recently acquired ability to see almost equally well night or day, and at greater depths of water. This had been made possible through the "invention" of a marvelous pigment called rhodopsin, or visual purple.

The basic parts of the retinas of the first teleostean fishes were much the same as the present-day fishes. The retina contained two kinds of light-receiving visual cells called rods and cones, microscopic in size and shaped roughly as their names suggest. Only rods were present in the retinas of the more primitive fishes, but, over a long period of time, some of these rods changed into cones.

Cones were, and are, used in the bright light of day, and each was connected to the brain by a separate nerve fiber, a sort of private line that transmitted clear and detailed pictures. On the other hand, the remaining rods, used mostly at night or in dim places, were connected to the nerve fibers in groups, rather like a party line, and the pictures they sent to the brain were inclined to be fuzzy and weak.

Nature, in order to improve on this, poured the miracle chemical porphyropsin, or visual red, into the rods of primitive vertebrates, where it accumulated to a high concentration in dim light or the darkness of night, giving the rods a far greater sensitivity to what light there was.

Rhodopsin (visual purple), a similar chemical, is found in the retinas of mammals (including man), birds, reptiles, amphibians, and most sea fishes, but fresh-water fishes—lampreys and larval amphibians—have the red porphyropsin in their rods. This is thought to be linked in some way with the spawning habits of fresh-water fishes. Certain sea fishes which swim up fresh-water rivers to spawn may have the fresh-water type of visual red in their retinas, others have a mixture of purple and red.

The accumulation of visual purple in the rods makes it possible for eyes to adapt to darkness, as they do when we humans enter a movie theater from a brightly lit street, and must wait a moment or so until our eyes "get used to the dark" so that we can find our seats. During this dark adaptation, the human eye becomes about ten thousand times more sensitive to light than when it is adapted to brightly illuminated surroundings.

Anyone who is deficient in vitamin A makes visual purple more slowly, and even if he remains out in the dark night for a long time his eyes will not adapt as they should, and he is what is known as night-blind.

Night-blindness is the earliest symptom of a lack of vitamin A, which is stored in the liver, and which can be obtained by eating liver, carrots, and similar everyday foods. The early Greeks, Romans, Chinese, and Egyptians were all aware that liver was the cure for night-blindness, and Hippocrates prescribed the rather awful expedient of eating an entire raw ox liver with honey. However, if you already have a sufficient supply of vitamin A in your makeup, you can eat liver and carrots until you never want to set eyes on either one again, and your vision will not be any better than it ever was.

So the fish suspended that night beneath the lunar rainbow could see food and enemies during most of the day and night. In fact, as it rested there, swayed by the currents, it was well aware of some appetizing little fish that were darting to and fro on one side of it, and of a much larger enemy fish swimming in menacing circles below.

Then one of the most wonderful days in the history of eyes dawned in a soft line of luminous gray above the horizon.

The newly landed mossy coverings of the shoreline rocks, which only a short while before had been dark as the night sky, turned gray. A clump of algal seaweed, stranded on the beach by a high tide, and already rooted and showing signs of becoming the fronded "feather plant" which was the first fern, stood blackly against the growing light, and the sea became a sheet of hammered steel.

Suddenly, in a glorious burst of light, the sun rose above the water, and the fish knew its miracle.

The sunshine sank into the eye of the fish, dispersing and weakening the visual purple in the retinal rods until it was a pale, yellowish pink, and the fish became dazzled and bewildered. Then it was, for the first time in the world, that the cones, working with a new compartment in their partner, the brain, disclosed the daylight world clearly and in an intricate and completely new beauty—color.

Slowly, the dark little clump of fernlike seaweed on the

shore took on the golden hues of the sunlight, the first color on earth, yellow. As the light increased, the gray-looking moss revealed itself in exquisitely delicate traceries of green and coral pink, like fine embroidery on the purple rocks at the base of which the lapping sea, white-frilled, shaded from a lovely turquoise green to dark jade where the water deepened.

The rain ceased, and the lunar rainbow was gone with the night, but not far from where it had been, glowing against the blue sky, between the eyes of the fish and the sun, seven concentric arcs shimmered, almost impercep-tibly, one into another. The top arc was a flaming red and melted downward into lesser arcs of orange, yellow, green, blue, indigo, and violet. Behind them the sky appeared darker, and then beyond and around this darker space, a second bow spread, fainter than the first and with the order of colors reversed, the red being on the low inside arc and the violet uppermost. As if this were not mysterious and beautiful enough, small complementary bands of color played about the centers of the inner edge of the first arc and the outer edge of the second, and the whole was a great marvel.

No structural changes had taken place in the rock plants, the sea, or the after-rain moisture in the atmosphere since the dark of night, yet they had thrown off their drab grays and blacks and were seen in all the colors of the rainbow. How? What is color?

Color does not really exist, in fact. It is sensed by the eyes and brain, as distinct from form or light and shade. It is a refinement of vision, an addition to the series of visual sensibilities that have evolved from the light-sensitive, all-seeing body of the first living creature. Color, like beauty, exists only in the mind of the beholder.

This is rather hard to accept, but it is nonetheless true. The rainbow by night was only a silvery wraith, the yellow shore plant, at the break of dawn, was black, and the moss gray, so that the lovely hues they took on after sunrise could scarcely have really belonged to them.

Through intensive research that led up to and on from the work of Sir Isaac Newton, it has been decided that color is a sensation excited by the action of rays of light of various definite wave lengths upon the retina of the eye, upon the cones.

Newton took a prism, a piece of crystal bounded in part by two plane faces which are not parallel, and by passing a beam of white light through it he split that beam up into all the colors of the rainbow—the spectrum—which seemed to prove that color was a property of the light itself. But physicists have since discovered that the luminous colors are only one part of the spectrum of radiation—that heat and other properties are included, and the spectrum as it is known now ranges from the long radio waves, through infrared to the visible light waves, and on again to the shorter waves of ultraviolet and X rays.

The rod cells of the eye, in the first light of pre-dawn, give colorless impressions, but as the intensity of the light waves increases, the cone cells can respond to color, first to yellow before there is sufficient light for them to react to blue, green, or red.

We do not yet know much about how retinal cones work to produce good vision in bright light. The cones, unlike the rods, contain little or no visual purple. They do appear to contain iodopsin and cyanopsin, violet and bluish visual pigments, which may account for their peculiar sensitivity to light. Yet these, it would seem, must be much less sensitive than visual purple or they would be dispersed and useless in daytime. Even less is known about how cones produce a sense of color, beyond the fact that some chemical change must take place in them in response to various wave lengths of radiant energy, which is sent on by means of electrical impulses to a special part of the brain.

Structural differences in the eyes of various animals affect their sense of color, and therefore sometimes even change the habits of the animals.

We see seven colors in the rainbow, but it is believed that birds see a much brighter bow, particularly at the red end of the spectrum. Frogs and cats are color-blind. Bees are aware of blue, insensitive to red, but possibly can see far into the violet and ultraviolet. Certain teleostean fishes see in color, but to what extent and how much other animals can do this, whether some are partly or completely color-blind, remains the subject of a tremendous amount of research, the subtleties of the various tests making decision extremely difficult.

Just as musical sounds differ in pitch, loudness, and quality, so do colors differ in hue, tint, and shade. All *hues* can be produced by combining pairs of primary colors in different proportion. The addition of white alters the *tint* without affecting the hue. If the color be darkened by adding black, or by diminishing the illumination, a variation of *shade* is made.

In certain cases, habit can modify or increase color sense. A person with normal eyesight can distinguish about one hundred and sixty color variations in sunlight, yet all these shades can be made up by various blendings of the three primary colors—red, green, and violet. (Artists, who work with pigments and not *light* colors, consider the primaries to be red, yellow, and blue.) According to Goethe, the Italian mosaic workers used fifteen thousand varieties of hues, each variety comprising fifty tints, an almost incredible awareness of color.

Color vision may depend not only on the cones, but on their nerve connections as well. We humans do not all see colors combined from the three primaries, and those who do not are termed color-blind. This is rather misleading, because nearly all "color-blind" people can see many colors, but generally they confuse red with green, and vice versa. Color-blindness occurs in about four per cent of men and four-tenths per cent of women, the latter's habits rendering color vision more important to them. Color-blindness is incurable, and can be inheritable in the male line of a family through females possessing a perfect sense of color.

The colors of all objects seen by the eye vary according to the objects' reaction to white light. Newton showed that white light could be broken up by a prism into the spectral colors of the rainbow, and therefore white is not a simple color but is the color of daylight, and probably owes its apparent purity to the fact that it is the average color of the light that fills the eye when at rest.

If you look closely at soap bubbles in a dishpan, you will see them in all the colors of the rainbow, but from a little distance they appear to be white, owing to the combined effect upon the eye of all the colors—a sort of reversal of the breaking down of white light into colors.

The varied colors of objects seen are not due to any property they themselves possess, but simply to the degree in which, by means of the various textures of which they are made, they absorb white light, or scatter it in all directions, or, in the case of transparent bodies, transmit it.

In ordinary opaque bodies, some of the light coming to them is irregularly reflected or scattered from their surfaces. A white object is one which *reflects* nearly all the light colors; a black object *absorbs* nearly all of them. A body which reflects only a portion of the light, and which shows no particular hue more than another, is called gray. If you paint a wooden wall panel with shiny white paint, which reflects much light, it will appear white, and if alongside it you paint the wall with a mat white paint, which reflects less light than the shiny white, the second panel will appear gray. This knowledge has been used in many different ways by interior decorators.

Gold metal looks yellow under ordinary circumstances, but if arranged to reflect the light many times from its surface, it appears ruby red. Yet if a strong light is transmitted through thin gold leaf, it appears green.

Heat will affect color, changing it from red to orange, yellow, and white as the heat increases and the wave lengths change.

A highly polished table top, whether opaque or transparent, when illuminated with white light and viewed from the proper angle, will reflect the light regularly and appear whitish, showing only a little of the color of its material.

Colored transparent objects vary in hue and shade according to their size. A conical glass filled with a red liquid usually appears yellow at the bottom, and shades through orange up to red at the top, because the light is transmitted directly through the small base, but is reflected back again at the larger top.

Translucence of a surface is due to light's being scattered by minute imbedded particles or irregularities. Some fibrous specimens of gypsum, for instance, are translucent in the direction of the fibers, and practically opaque when looked at from the opposite direction.

A small amount of colored powder, such as dry paint, is usually much lighter in tint than the same powder in bulk, as the light is reflected back after transmission through only a few layers in the small amount. For the same reason, the powders of transparent substances are opaque.

Thickness will affect color. A thin white windowpane is transparent and remains white all over, but a thick white glass shelf, viewed from certain angles, is more opaque and bright green. The color of the sky is blue because of the vastness of it and the scattering of light by small, suspended particles, which is most effective in the case of the shorter light waves (blue). Again, pure water, although nearly colorless, in large masses appears bluish green, and most of us have seen how the color of the sea darkens as the coastal areas are left behind and the water deepens.

Anyone who has had anything to do with stage lighting is aware that under certain artificial conditions, colors can be changed. Theatrical limelights, played on white costumes, can produce any of the colors of the gelatin windows through which the light is thrown, or any combination can be made with one or more colored lights on a dress, face, or piece of scenery of another color—a form of painting with light, which, however, must use the *light* primary colors and not the *painter's* primaries.

The primitive animals gained much from this new addition to life. Color camouflage became one of the chief weapons of defense.

The sun had not long risen on that particular day when the first of all living creatures to become aware of color, our teleostean fish, felt the need of food. Swimming in the direction of the smaller fishes that it had noticed before dawn, it was puzzled to find them no longer there. One minute they had been in plain sight, the next they had vanished. This was because their general coloring was a translucent bluish-green that merged perfectly with the color of the water. The same bewilderment was experienced by the large enemy fish below, who for some time had had an eye on the teleostean. The big fish could no longer see its prey, because the teleostean's coloring, darkest on its back, and shading into lighter colors on its sides that finally faded into clear white on its belly, obliterated the appearance of solidity, which is due to shadow. The light coming from above made the back of the fish appear to be the same color as the surrounding water, while the white belly neutralized the dark shadow which otherwise would have been plainly visible there.

Some crabs take on the colors of the matter over which they crawl, and mollusks the coloring of the coral on which they live.

The coloration of the surface of animals is caused by

pigmentation, or by a certain structure or texture of their surface (shell, skin, fur, and so forth), by means of which the light falling upon them, or reflected through transparent layers, undergoes diffraction. In some cases, pigments are built up in the tissues of the animals; in others they appear to come more or less directly from the food. In certain fish, and in some other creatures, coloring is immediately associated with the nervous system, and is heightened at times not only through sexual desires to attract, but under the excitement due to fighting or feeding.

That vision is important to fish in controlling their life-saving camouflage is proved by an experiment made with certain fish which, at the approach of danger, assume colored spots that merge with their surroundings. The eyes of these fish were painted over with a harmless but opaque substance, so that they were temporarily blinded, and they were then released in the vicinity of enemies. The safe-guard spots did not appear.

However, color is sometimes used in the opposite sense —to make the owner conspicuous, a warning to possible attackers. Sea anemones fly brilliant flags of color to scare off their enemies, and the bright claws of certain crabs attract the initial attack, when the crab throws them off and, detached, they continue to snap and hold the attention of the attacker while the crab escapes.

Certain animals, especially the crustaceans, make use of

the defense and warning colors of others. The English hermit crab, for one, carries the highly colored and poisonous sea anemone on its shell. Each species of animal which falls into a group with common warning signals contributes to save the lives of other members of the group.

These are just a few random glimpses into the changes brought about in life by the advent of color sense, one of the greatest achievements of the eye and brain in partnership. The astonishingly varied use of color by the higher animals, for the defense and increase of their kind, was yet to come.

So, vision for the teleostean fishes was much more than the registering of light, movement, form, balance, proper focus, perspective, and color. The brain, working with the eye, was beginning to perceive the *meaning* of objects seen, and to remember them and take suitable action when re-encountering them.

This would seem to be close to the ultimate in visual needs, but an apparent calamity, some three hundred million years ago, forced the seeing eye to face strange new conditions, for which it had to rebuild itself almost entirely.

Chapter 5

SIGHT COMES ASHORE

A Devonian crossopterygian (Osteolepis) about to explore the land in search of bigger and better pools. Fishes such as this, and the lungfish (Dipterus) beneath the surface of the water, struggling to traverse a foreign environment by means of their strong lobed fins, their eyes exposed to hitherto unknown light and dryness, pioneered for later forms of life which were to live completely outside the sea.

In order that these two examples might be clearly portrayed, one of the principles of optics has been left out of this picture —the refraction of light. In passing from one medium to another, such as from air to water, light is refracted, or bent, so that objects half submerged in water appear to be bent beneath the surface. If looked at from above the pool, this osteolepis's tail would seem to be slightly out of line with the rest of its body.

The hour of departure has arrived, and we go our ways—I to die, you to live. Which is the better, God only knows.

—Socrates

THE SEA is usually a gentle place in which to live, so far as temperature is concerned. In hot weather, the surface heats slowly, in cold it cools off gradually. (The "cold" blood of fishes changes with the temperature.) It is also true that the supply of food provided by the sea seldom fluctuates.

In such a static environment there was little stimulus for many of the early fishes to advance beyond a certain stage, no need for their nervous systems to develop toward the higher mentality later reached by land animals living under constantly changing and challenging conditions. The only thing that most of the primitive sea creatures could do was diversify their species; yet some of these physical changes were to equip certain ones among the fishes so that they could become vertebrate pioneers in a strange new place, half water, half earth. They were to become amphibians.

As time went by in thousands of centuries, the bony fishes divided into two major groups—the subclass Actinopterygii, topped by the teleosteans, with which we are now familiar, and the subclass Choanichthyes. These latter are the more important of the two, for they include the order Crossopterygii, from which it is thought most land vertebrates are descended, and the order Dipnoi—lungfishes which survive today in the tropical regions of Australia, Africa, and South America.

Choanichthyes may have some parts which the actinopterygii do not have: internal nostrils associated with lung-breathing, fleshy-lobed fins suitable for development into land limbs, and scales which in early forms showed features to be expected in the ancestors of amphibians. It was once thought by some that amphibians evolved from the lungfishes, but now the lungfishes are considered to be more like "cousins" to our fish forebears.

Based on facts we have pieced together from various clues, this is probably how the great step from sea to land began:

One particularly hot, dry period, about three hundred million years ago, a dipnoan and a crossopterygian lived peacefully enough in a fresh-water pool, the smallest of a chain only a few yards one from another. Around the edges of the pools grew rushes and jointed canes, and giant ferns rising some fifty feet into the air, remote descendants of the seaweeds once brought ashore by the tides.

The crossopterygian's scales gleamed beneath the shallow water, as it slowly waved its lobe-shaped fins to and fro. The dipnoan was less conspicuous, but its blunt, snake-like mouth, with massive jaws and flat teeth designed for crushing snail shells, was formidable.

The sun, impartial giver of life and death, blazed down upon the little pool, and, as the days passed, what water there was in it slowly evaporated. Soon there was not more than an inch or two above the ooze of the bottom. The water became thick and rank, and further impurities were added to it by seepage from the soil. Another day, and there remained nothing but mud, rapidly caking under the pitiless sunshine. The two fishes began to use their lungs, struggling to draw from the air the oxygen they had previously obtained mostly from water, but each took a different way out of the frightful drought.

The dipnoan dug itself deep into the slime beneath the pool bottom, to lie there buried beneath the hardened surface, almost in a state of suspended animation. It remained imprisoned there, month after month, breathing only a little by means of its lungs. It was waiting for the rains to come and the waters to rise again and possibly release it before it died—an endurance test few could survive.

The crossopterygian refused to dig itself into such a blind alley. Using its strong lobed fins as a primitive form of legs, it dragged itself up over the edge of the empty pool and came to land.

Some have said that the first faint hint of vertebrates' land legs came into being to enable their owners to escape from enemies—but the lobe-finned fishes were among the largest and most aggressive in their native pools. Others have said that vertebrates' legs were developed in order to gain new food supplies—but both the early amphibians and their fish ancestors were carnivorous, and there was little animal food on land at that time. Yet others have proffered the opinion that fishes came to land "lured by atmospheric oxygen"—but the ancestral lobe fin had developed competent lungs in the water, and the only effort it had to make to obtain as much oxygen as it needed was to push its head above the surface of the pool.

It seems more probable that those first leglike fins were used simply to enable the crossopterygian *to stay in the water to which it was accustomed.* It dragged itself painfully over the dry earth, away from its ruined home, hopefully searching for bigger and better pools. As it went, slowly stumbling over rocks and pebbles, the parched canes and rushes rustled overhead, huge cockroaches as long as a forefinger barred its path, and iridescent dragonflies, with a wingspread of more than two feet, swooped down to take a closer look at the newcomer. Apart from the whispering vegetation, there was no sound, no chirping or buzzing or howling or chattering, for this was ages before the first voice.

In silence, then, inch by inch, the crossopterygian progressed. All through the night it crawled stubbornly on, pausing only occasionally to rest, until at last, just before dawn, it came to the next pool—larger and not yet dried up—and swiftly slipped into the comforting water.

That epic journey, that heroic struggle by means of a new and inadequate form of locomotion in a strange environment by a vertebrate from the water, made possible much fuller, wider ways of life for living things to come.

In the world-wide tropical heat of the ages that followed, the various kinds of fishes with lungs were stranded again and again by droughts. In time, those that did not bury themselves in the mud like the dipnoi became adapted to living in the swamps surrounding the pools, rather than in the actual water, and later to living on drier land. One small, gudgeon-like fish, alive today, uses its pectoral fins for land locomotion. It is called *Periophthalamus,* because its eyes are on top of its head so that it can look all around on land (from the Greek word, *peri,* a prefix meaning "all round"). Another similar fish, the *Anableps tetrophthalamus* (Greek, *tetr-,* a combining form meaning "having four, or four parts"), has two pupils in each eye, one adapted for seeing in water, the other in air.

As certain fishes like these gradually broke the ties that held them to their ancestral seas and rivers, their fins adapted until they became a more practical aid to locomotion on land. The original spade-shaped fin was neat and smooth-edged, looking as though it had been finely accordion-pleated. Slowly, slowly, the smooth edge became

fringed. After a longer time, the fringes apparently separated at the tips and concentrated into four more or less
definite points, and there is one theory that finally the
bones at the ends of the fins gathered the fringed points
around them and became primitive feet.

On a sandstone slab in the museum of Yale University
is a single footprint from a creature of this period, called
Thinopus antiquus, the first recorded footprint on earth,
recognized millions of years later. It shows only two completely formed "fingers" (or "toes"), with an indication
of a third undeveloped one.

The brains of these land pioneers were not capable of
giving long, studious attention to what was happening to
their owners, nor to the strange new surroundings and conditions. Most of the new necessary reactions and movements came instinctively, aided by gradually improving
methods of locomotion.

It has been thought by some scientists that the brain
always developed first, and that it was through the brain's
realization of need from time to time that it went into
action and brought about the formation of new lungs,
limbs, and so forth. If we go back over what we have
already talked about here, we will see that this is absurd.
The brain may *forward* a necessary change, as it did when
it outpocketed the sunken eyespots in the first fish head,
but it does not actually create physical matter, including
its own. It is no more than a receiving station for sensa-

tions and a sending station for action on sensations received. The brains of higher animals are also storehouses for impressions received and actions taken, a sort of file cabinet which can be referred to at will. Professor Tilly Edinger, of Harvard University, in 1948 showed that the growth of the brain tends to *follow* in evolution.

The first vertebrates to remain on land for any length of time were immediate descendants of the crossopterygians. They are known as amphibians, from two Greek roots meaning "like on both sides," because they have always lived in water as well as on land. Amphibian eggs were laid in fresh-water pools, the kind inhabited by the lungfishes. The bodies of the very first amphibians were fishlike, resembling their ancestors, but this shape was lost in later types.

Ages after the astonishing journey of the crossopterygian in search of water, a characteristic baby amphibian, in appearance rather like our tadpole, hatched out of an egg. Its body, mostly belly, grew to a little less than six inches long, its head was wide and flat, and on top of its head were three eyes, set in a triangle, two parallel nearest the front and one higher up. This third eye was not functional; it was simply the vestige of that third "eye" of the first vertebrate.

In the young, or larval, stages, the amphibian breathed through its gills, just like the fish before it, and could not leave the water, but before long its lungs developed and its gills disappeared. The baby rose to the surface of the pool, stuck its nose out, and breathed the air deeply down through its nasal passages into its mouth and lungs. Then, using its beautiful new legs, it came to the edge of the pool and made its first landing.

It was an unhappy landing.

At the very outset, the amphibian was almost knocked off its feet by something that completely bewildered it. This was gravity. For the first time in its experience, inherited or actual, the little creature was left without the support of buoyant water. Its nursery had been a pleasant place in which to live, requiring little effort to navigate in, but now the entire weight of its body descended upon its wobbly new legs, and both balance and movement called for tremendous effort.

Staggering under this discovery, the amphibian—an ichthyostegid—felt the need of sustenance. It noticed a small, juicy water worm nearby—that is, at first glance it seemed to be nearby, but then it suddenly jumped, apparently without making a move, and continued to be elusive in the most disconcerting manner. Something was wrong with the amphibian's eyes. They had far too much focusing power.

At the same time, the poor "baby" was blasted by blinding, searing heat. Without the protection of water, it seemed in for a serious case of sunburn. Its skin began to dry, but worst of all was the effect upon its eyes, particularly the delicate retina.

Many sea creatures, stranded by the tide on the seashore, have come up against gravity and drying heat in their struggles to get back into the water. Some of them do manage to twist and flop their way home, but others, such as the jellyfish, just give up and rapidly evaporate to small circular films on the sand. It was not in the amphibian's makeup to allow this to happen to it.

Back in the days of its infancy, in its watery cradle, the amphibian never had to worry about the burning effect of the sun's ultraviolet rays, because water absorbs all of them. Now, however, it was faced with a serious situation, the possible failure of its adventurous arrival on soil. A dry eye, be it amphibian or human, is most easily infected, and can even cause the death of its owner. Nature once again had to take a great step.

The lungfish, struggling to survive through their pioneer treks from pool to pool, had faced the problem of dry eyes. The comfort which they had inherited from their sea ancestors—the lubrication and cleansing of eyes by the waters washing over them—was a valuable asset. The wonder was that they *could* take it with them, when they passed on to another environment. They carried small portions of sea between the lens and cornea of their eyes—a precious *aqueous humor* descended in part from a viscous fluid which, millions of years before, had eased the eyes of the primitive fishes when they first sank into protective pits.

This fluid within the eyeball was inherited by the amphibians, but the outer surface of the cornea had to be kept moist, too, otherwise it lost its transparency and some of its smoothness. To bring this about, lids made of skin, lined with conjunctiva, grew from the upper and lower edges of the eye sockets. The lower lid, thinner than the other, was the only movable one.

From the time, long ago, when the conjunctiva first turned inward to facilitate the mobility of early fish eyes, there had always been microscopic slime glands imbedded in its membrane. These now concentrated in the corners of the amphibian's eyes, and their secretion, spread at regular intervals over the cornea by the raising and lowering of the eyelid, prevented the eyes from drying out and becoming infected. More glands in the orbit around the eyes secreted different fluids, some of them to feed the cornea, which had no blood vessels to give it sustenance, others to lubricate the margins of the lids so that they could function smoothly.

The difficulty our amphibian had in seeing its worm properly was due to the fact that as yet it was not accustomed to looking through air, a very different matter from looking through water. In fishes, as we have seen, the refractive power of the cornea was nullified by the almost equal power of the surrounding water, but the difference between the refractive powers of air and the cornea is considerable, air's index being practically zero. The amphibian's cornea was the most effective refractive surface in its entire eye, so that, with the added power of the lens itself, the eye focused much too strongly, and the "image" of the worm rebounded off the retina into the part between the retina and the lens, known as the vitreous.

In the fishes proper, the lens protruded through the pupil. The amphibian found that he could adjust his focusing power by pulling the lens back a little into the vitreous part of the eyeball, which "pressed" the image of the worm back into its proper place on the retina. Then the baby amphibian neatly grabbed the now clearly visible worm, and had dinner.

In spite of a good meal, with all these new sensations and problems to overcome it is not surprising that the little amphibian "burst into tears," the first creature on earth to do so. Actually, although it shed tears, it did not do so emotionally. It was left for man to *weep*. The amphibian's tears were literally cleansing, carrying off all waste products from the eye through a newly formed tear duct into the nearest available space, the nose.

Amphibians may be divided, roughly, into two classes— the older, with tails, alive today in the form of salamanders and newts, and the less primitive tailless type, such as our frogs and toads. The first amphibians were generally very large, compared to those existing now (although the modern Chinese salamander is exceptional, being about five feet long), and most of them inherited the blunt heads of their crossopterygian ancestors.

Among the rich vegetation on shore at that time, food was abundant, and the terrestrial vertebrates were not yet sufficiently diversified so that they preyed upon one another to live. For more than a million years, the amphibians lived peacefully enough, grew larger, and multiplied in the damp heat of the period. Having no enemies, there was no reason for them to hide, and they basked in the light of day—purely diurnal creatures.

As they became more accustomed to the air, they found that it had several advantages. Among these was the clarity and low light-absorbing quality of air, which greatly improved vision. Once the amphibian's eyes fully adjusted to the new environment, it could see much farther than the fishes ever did, and everything looked brighter.

Although modern amphibians are not diurnal, their eyes prove that their ancestors were. Each retinal cone in most of the modern amphibian's eyes holds a wonderful little filter, yellow in color and minute in size, but big in importance. Not only do these cone oil-droplets improve daytime vision, but they are enormously useful in tracing back the history of eyes. If any group of animals, for one reason or other during the course of evolution, fails to possess these droplets, none of their descendants can ever have them. Therefore, the fact that they are present in the retinal cones of present-day frogs seems to prove that the

ancestral armor-heads had them, too. Toads and salamanders have given up these yellow oil-droplets, and become
strictly nocturnal animals, because without the little sensi-
tivity-reducing filters they have to hide or sleep through
the revealing daylight hours.

Two priceless gifts come to us from the first froglike
creatures—one, the thumb, seen today still in its more or
less primitive form in the little *opponens* of the frog's
"hand"; the other, vocal cords.

Frogs' eyes have changed little throughout the ages.
One of the notable things about them, incidentally, is that
whenever the frog gets some unusually large piece of food
or other matter lodged in its throat, it can pull its eyes back
into their sockets and scrape its throat clear with them.

As this particular hot and steamy period approached its
end, about two hundred and fifty million years ago, the
amphibians adapted themselves more and more to living
in air alone. At the very end of the era, the climate became
drier, and the swamps and streams shrank so that the next
great class of vertebrates, the reptiles, lived entirely on
land. Another thing that furthered this advance was the
inconvenience experienced by the female amphibians
when they had to return to the water each year in order
to lay their eggs. The reptiles created a much better
method, which was far less trouble—the porous eggshell.
This shell not only protected their young, but contained
the necessary food for them as well, and could be safely

laid in the hollows of the land. Because of this extremely practical method of reproduction, the reptiles greatly increased in number, while the amphibians gradually decreased until today they are only a small group among the vertebrates.

The end of the age when amphibians were supreme was much like its beginning. The flat, swampy earth shook and heaved itself up once again into hills and mountains. The ocean bottoms sank to tremendous depths, and the seas retreated into them from the land. For the next two million years or so, a devastating cold gripped what would become Australia, South America, and Africa, almost to the equator. The few plants and animals the cold failed to kill sought sanctuary in the restricted belt of warmth, from which, in the slow course of time, there evolved a race of terrible monsters.

Chapter 6

THE AIMED EYES OF GONDWANALAND

The first voluntary eye movements, *aimed* vision, appeared in the early reptiles, millions of years ago. Here are some of these great beasts, watched for in fear by smaller reptiles and other newly evolved creatures of the primitive dry earth. In the foreground is *Tyrannosaurus rex*, the "king tyrant lizard." One of the largest of the carnivorous dinosaurs, it was the most destructive menace of its time (the Cretaceous period), excelling all others in ferocity and precise, speedy movement.

On the lake shoreline is a stegosaurus, a lumbering brute measuring about twenty feet from its jaw to its lethal, spiked tail-tip, and twelve feet from the ground to the top of its double bony comb. Its eyes were comparatively large, suggesting nocturnal habits, but the brain was remarkably small, even among dinosaurs.

A brontosaurus—the "thunder lizard," which often attained a length of seventy to eighty feet—is emerging from the lake, where it spends most of its time. Both the brontosaurus and the stegosaurus lived earlier than the tyrannosaurus, in the Jurassic period.

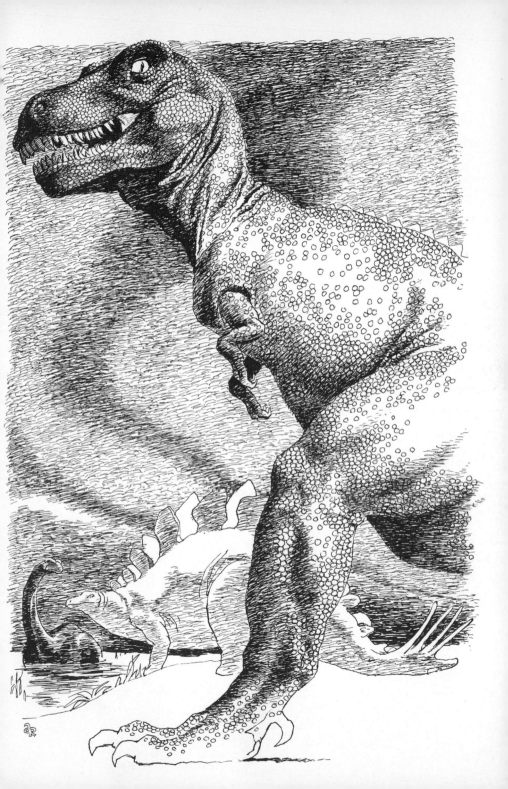

The earth hath bubbles, as the water has,
And these are of them:—Whither are they
vanished?
                    —William Shakespeare, *Macbeth*

ONCE there was an enormous land, a continent stretching for thousands of miles, joining what is now South Africa and India. Over much of it the Indian Ocean rolls today, but it has left traces in South America, Africa, and Australia. The geologists have named it Gondwanaland, and about two hundred million years ago it was the home and burial grounds of terrible toothed reptiles.

The frightful cold that killed off so many of the amphibians, and the plants among which they lived, left its mark on Gondwanaland. Huge boulders and smaller deposits were scattered over the soil by the glaciers, and the rocks were deeply scratched by the grinding ice. As the climate grew warm again, part of the interior of the huge continent was taken up by several large lakes, their beds a great layer of sandstone and marsh.

The climate became drier, and those plants which had not died became much changed, evolving into cycads and conifers, lepidodendrons, and sigillaria—the first trees in the world, leading to our palms, pines, junipers, cypresses, and giant redwoods. Later, some of the cycads and conifers died out, to be replaced by trees of harder, less fibrous wood, among them yews and cedars.

Two distinct floral regions appeared, northern and southern, the southern within the boundaries of Gondwanaland. There the original plants gave way to entirely new flora named Glossopteria, or tongue-fern, from its tongue-shaped, rather fleshy leaves.

The early horsetails reached a diameter of about two feet, and grew to between sixty and one hundred feet high, but many of them became extinct, together with the early ferns, and in place of them came the angiosperms, or flowering plants. These were the monocotyledons, ancestors of the grasses, sedges, and lilies, and the dicotyledons, from which came oaks, elms, roses, and all related trees, shrubs, and herbs.

The development of the land plants is important in the story of eyes, not only because they made up part of the landscape seen by each new form of eye, but because from time to time they provided, or fatally failed to provide, food for various animals. It is generally believed that as some of the more primitive growths disappeared, so did some of the creatures that relied on them for sustenance. Although the new flowering plants supplied good nourishment for certain animals alive toward the end of that era, they certainly would not have for any man alive today.

Night was dropping over the largest of the Gondwanaland lakes, in that part which is now South Africa. At the
base of a tall gingko—the "maidenhair" tree, the only one
of all the trees growing at that time which has survived
unchanged into our era—a colony of ants was perfecting
the laws and habits of their way of life which, ages later,
was to astonish and inspire men. A spider quivered its web
temptingly under a coned branch, and a caddisfly pupa bit
its way into existence, sawing at its larval envelope of silk-
cemented sand with strong mandibles. Scorpion flies and
dragonflies lanced the air in the wake of their prey. A line
of shining little beetles skittered into the canebrakes. A
grasshopper catapulted over some flowering herbs, and a
snake, dim-eyed, rippled luxuriously into a clear patch still
warm from the sun. As yet, there were no butterflies, but
some primitive wasps buzzed importantly here and there.
There was much activity around the lake that nightfall.

Suddenly, of one accord, all became absolutely still—all
but the spider, which rapidly shook its web into invisi-
bility. A warning was in the air—everything was on guard,
for this was the era when some of the larger land animals
had discovered for themselves the pleasures of cannibalism.

A short distance out on the lake, the surface broke, and
concentric circles rippled the water quickly to shore, where
it hit with angry slaps. Hearing these, the creatures which
had not yet found shelter for the night quickly sought it.
The snake could not hear the ominous water sounds, for

it had no proper ears; but although its sight that particular evening was not clear either, its active brain sensed the danger well enough.

This was the age when some amphibians were evolving into reptiles, and the snake was a legless, scaled creature— as yet, hair, fur, and feathers had not come into being—so it could not rub its rather delicate eyes or screen them with lashes to keep them clear. Its eyelids were reduced to mere lines of skin on the rims, but, like most reptiles, it had a third eyelid, called the nictitating membrane, which usually winks over the cornea from the inner corner slantingly up and backward, but in the snake's case became a permanently fixed transparent cover. This meant that, somewhat like those of the fishes, the snake's eyes unceasingly presented pictures to its active brain. However, it did not need motion blindness to help it to ignore these sights when it needed rest, because its pupils, instead of being round holes, were narrow slits which could be completely closed by muscular contraction of the iris, just as we close our eyelids. In the course of everyday life, the snake's transparent lids became somewhat clouded and scratched, but each time it shed its skin the eyelids went along too, revealing clear, shining new ones underneath.

The snake slid into the shelter of a crevice between two boulders. In the sand between the boulders and the lake a certain small, short-legged lizard was burrowing into the sand. As it dug itself into hiding, it constantly lubricated the corneas of its eyes by means of its thin, nictitating membranes, which did away with the necessity of winking its other eyelids and so momentarily losing vision. Even when the sand flying between its claws became too uncomfortable and forced it to close its opaque lids, it still could look out for danger, because in the center of its lower lid was a transparent disk through which it could see a little.

As full night descended, and slowly passed, the small creatures hidden in their various sanctuaries were aware of strange, horrible grunts and croakings, of long slithering sounds in the rushes, and the cracking of canes. Now and again the earth trembled to some enormous footfall, and more than once the dark intervals of silence were shattered by a frightful death scream.

When daylight, with tropical abruptness, again flooded the land, the lizard timorously raised its little head above the sand and looked around.

Its eyes were adapted for daytime, the retinas being composed entirely of cones. (Those modern reptiles which have become nocturnal have had to change some, or all, of their cones back into rods.) But the reptiles of which this lizard was one had greatly improved their retinas to meet the increasingly exacting demands of life on earth. They brought a number of their cones closely together into a small central patch on the retina, the *fovea centralis*. The retina at the fovea was much thinner than elsewhere, and the closely packed cones slender and tall, presenting much more surface for the reception of impressions. The result was finely detailed, *aimed* vision—the first voluntary eye movements, as opposed to reflex action, in animals in the direct line leading to man.

With the more loosely scattered cones on the periphery of its retinas, the lizard received a general impression of the sand and rocks around it, of the lush vegetation, the body of the lake, and some dark patches on the water. From previous experience, it knew that it had to watch out for those dark patches.

First, the lizard adjusted the focus of its eyes. Snakes, and some of the amphibians, push their lenses forward or pull them back to vary the focus, like some of the fishes, and the lenses are almost round balls; but reptiles (with the exception of snakes) have lenses which are only slightly curved on both sides. To see nearby objects, they make these curves much greater, bulging them through the pupils by compressing them with the iris and ciliary muscle at the base of the iris. The lenses are soft and elastic, so that when the pressure is released they go back to their original slender curve. This makes it possible for reptiles to see, with equal clarity, a distant horizon or a minute insect right beside them. Their eyes being set on each side of their heads, they do not see the same things with both eyes, as we do, but have a choice between two vistas. Their brains decide which one of the two they will concentrate on. Such a highly developed visual system could not be complete without the added improvement of color sense, and this the reptiles achieved, so becoming the first *land* animals capable of seeing in color.

Having adjusted the focus, the lizard aimed its fovea directly at the dark patches on the lake, one after another, and its fears materialized in clear-cut detail.

The shallows near the shore, and indeed much of the shore itself, were crowded with monsters. Some were small, others were ten to thirteen feet in length, but all were horrible to see. Their heads ranged in size from a few inches to about three feet long, and their horny jaws ended in turtle-like beaks. Their eyes were large, adapted for the eternal twilight of the canebrakes and jungle, or for night-prowling, and from their teeth, which were different from those of other reptiles, they got their name—anomodont, or "irregular-toothed." As they went, those among them that had not found enough food during the night on land attacked each other with awful ferocity, and the air was filled with their cries and the sound of combat.

A later form of terrible mammal-like reptiles were the theriodonts, or "beast-toothed," whose dental structures were suited to the devouring of insects and plants as well as flesh. Their hind legs were long, and their locomotion comparatively swift. It is believed that from these terrible creatures, living in Gondwanaland, there evolved the next group of land animals, the mammals.

The reign of the great dinosaurs lasted over ninety million years, during which time they increased and spread over the world. At first, they were not particularly large, but it does not always take great size to produce a terrifying appearance.

Generally speaking, the dinosaurs are divided into groups according to their pelvis, teeth, and feet. There are the "bird-hipped" and the "lizard-hipped," the "bird-footed" and the "lizard-footed." Some had strong claws, others flat nails or hoofs. Certain ones among them had teeth for mastication; others either had no teeth or just a few teeth at the back of their horny beaks.

Dinosaurs like the "flexible lizard" (*Camptosaurus*) walked on their two hind legs; others, like the stegosaurs, with a double alternating row of great spade-shaped projections along their backs, walked on four legs and, being less ferocious than most of their contemporaries, developed armor for protection in battle.

The tiny brains of the stegosaurs, weighing less than three ounces, could not do much to direct their enormous bulk of around twenty feet long and nine feet high, but they did have some enlarged nerves in a vertebral bone near the pelvis, which acted as centers of reflex action for control of their hind legs and death-dealing spiked tails.

Another armored type, the *Ankylosaurus*, had bony plates over its head which helped to guard the eyes from attack by teeth and claws.

Dinosaur brains were all small in comparison to their bodies. The huge *Triceratops*, a rhinoceros-like animal with a horn over each eye and sometimes one at the end of the snout (although much time was to elapse before the true rhinos, being mammals, were to arrive), weighed over ten tons, but its brain weighed less than two pounds.

The dinosaur *Iguanodon,* eighteen to thirty feet long and about fourteen feet high, had forelimbs that vaguely suggested hands. Where our thumbs are it had more or less pointed projections, believed by some to have been used for holding on to or pulling up its plant food.

During the millions of years when the dinosaurs dominated all life, they lived in surroundings so completely suited to them that they specialized only to meet their present needs, and were not adaptable to any future change in environment.

As the era drew to its close, some of the reptiles increased in size and number until the competition for existence became so intense that some of them gave up and returned to the sea to live, as happened later to some mammals and even birds.

One of the first to do so was the *Ichthyosaurus,* or "fish reptile." This creature, ten feet or more in length, looked rather like a dolphin, the body shape being completely reconverted to that of a fish. It had four flippers, vestiges of the limbs it had used on shore, and most interesting eyes. They were very large, and the pupil and iris were surrounded by concentric layers of thin bone. This optic armor very likely served several purposes. It would seem to have been a protection for the eyeball from the waves when the animal swam on the surface, and when the ichthyosaurus dived it probably protected it from pressure. It certainly aided in regulation of vision for objects near and far. This was accomplished by contraction or relaxation of the plates, another way of focusing pictures on the retina. The enormous eyes are evidence that the ichthyosaurs depended very largely on the sense of vision.

The end of Gondwanaland was violent. It literally broke into pieces. Terrific earthquakes occurred, due to faulting, and whole blocks of the country were let down and flooded by the oceans. Other blocks, called "horsts," miraculously remained unharmed, one of them being the island of Madagascar, another the African mountain, Ruwenzori.

Huge numbers of the terrible toothed reptiles and other land life perished in the long-lasting calamity. The limited brains of the highly specialized theriodonts failed to provide them with methods by which they might have met the emergencies. Only those few with a glimmer of intelligence, who had not specialized beyond any hope of adapting to new conditions, proved capable of survival, gradually changing in form until they became mammals.

The reason for the end of the age of reptiles all over the world is far from fully understood. Great upheavals in the earth's surface, such as those which broke up Gondwanaland, were possibly the basic factor, when vast areas of marsh and lagoons, which provided food for the dinosaurs, disappeared. Violent changes in climate caused new types of plants to appear which were probably not suitable for the somewhat inefficient teeth of the herbivorous monsters. As these died out, their flesh-eating relatives, who fed upon them, would also become extinct.

However, there were two important shoots which grew from the reptilian tree—the pterosaurs and the first birds.

After a great stretch of time, winged vision developed to the point where it was to excel all others—even, in a sense, that of man.

Chapter 7

WINGED VISION

Millions of years before the birds, certain reptiles took to the air on planes of stretched skin, some with a spread of nearly thirty feet. One of these, *Pteranodon,* is shown at the bottom of the opposite page, behind an early dinosaur from which it sprang.

Immediately above is *Archaeopteryx,* or "ancient flyer," about the size of a crow, toothed, clawed, its tail much longer than its body, and with clawed fingers on the edge of its wings. Although its skeleton closely resembled that of a reptile, the presence of body feathers proved it to be a true bird, ancestor of those we know, including the nocturnal owl, shown here above a cross section of its eye, and the eagle, also with a cross section. In these sections, the striped area in the vitreous humor, between the retina and the lens, is the pecten, a pleated vascular projection for the conveyance of nutritive fluids. Pectens are present in most reptiles and all birds, except the flightless kiwi (*Apteryx*) of New Zealand.

At the left center is the skull of a bird, showing the bony, overlapping sclerotic plates.

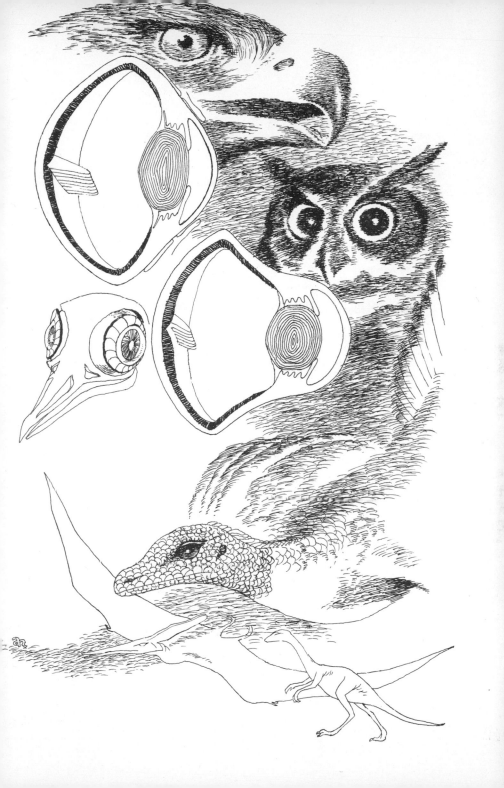

> *It was a hand or sound*
> *In the long ago that glided the dark door wide*
> *And there outside on the bread of the ground*
> *A she bird rose and rayed like a burning bride.*
> *A she bird dawned, and her breast with snow*
> *and scarlet downed.*
> —Dylan Thomas, "A Winter's Tale"

IN THE dim light among the giant ferns and canebrakes, a weird black shape glided out, batlike, on enormous skin wings, in search of food. The eerie creature was a pterosaur—the first vertebrate to fly.

Exactly how the power of flight came about remains a mystery, but the winged reptiles, or order pterosaurs (of which the pterodactyls, or "wing-fingered," are a suborder) were the first reptiles known to us to leave the earth, millions of years before the birds.

Compared to that of birds or insects, the flight apparatus of the pterosaurs was entirely individual. The primitive birds had three "fingers" to each wing, and the bones attached to them were similar to those of the human hand, both in design and comparative size. The pterosaurs, however, had four fingers, with a very long hook attached to the "little" finger which supported most of the stretched, scaleless skin that acted as a plane for flight. Some of these "little" fingers were about five feet long, holding a wing-spread of nearly thirty feet. Other structural differences in the skeletons of birds and pterosaurs definitely show that the two, although branching from the same reptilian stem, have solved the problem of flight differently. Although their skulls and brains were pretty much alike, the brains being very small in relation to their entire bodies, the pterosaurs glided about by means of a leathery membrane, but the birds developed feathers that not only formed the flight surface, but also insulated their bodies from their environment, aiding them to survive climatic changes with which the pterosaurs probably could not cope.

There is, however, a similarity between the eyes of birds and pterosaurs. The pterosaurs are believed to have had excellent eyesight. At the front and back of the whites of their eyes (the sclera) they had from ten to seventeen bony, overlapping discs, the sclerotic plates, somewhat like those horny outer plates of the aquatic ichthyosaurus. Because of the large size of the pterosaurean eye sockets, found in fossils, the pioneer paleontologist Cuvier thought that their habits were mostly nocturnal, so probably their retinas were made up mostly of rods, and very likely they were unaware of color; but this is uncertain.

Their general appearance was somewhat similar to bats, although very much larger, and their heads were triangular in shape—but the two animals are distinctly individual. Bats are mammals, not descended from the pterosaurs.

They are the only mammals able to fly, unless you consider man as now possessed of that power, and probably their flying apparatus developed in the way that some squirrels and lemur-like creatures (the *Galeopithecus*) have grown a "flying-membrane."

Bats have poor vision, for which they compensate as they fly by squeaking, and their highly sensitive ears pick up the sound waves of those squeaks as they bounce back from objects ahead or around—a sort of radar system. The fact that bats cannot trust to eyesight alone in flight is proved, for example, by the death of some red bats which not long ago crashed against the Empire State Building in New York, their warning signals apparently confused by the television signals emanating from that tower.

When first the pterosaurs flew, they were not alone in the skies. There were the flying *in*vertebrates—primitive insects living on dry land, as the bees, moths, and butterflies do today, although these types of insects did not exist then, and those living half in water and half on land, as the caddis and dragonflies did then and do now.

Insects can have any number of eyes, from two to fifty. Set as firmly in their sockets as bulbs in lamps, they are absolutely immovable, unblinking, and short-sighted. The insects must move their entire heads to see anything outside their original range of vision, and in those where the head is set closely to the body, the entire thorax must be turned.

The human eye remains the same from birth to death, but the insect eye changes considerably, sometimes both in structure and number, between the larval stage and adulthood. The adult eyes are divided into two types, simple and compound, and sometimes both are present in the same insect. Simple eyes may number from one to forty-eight, and have only a single lens. The compound eyes, made up of between two and about thirty thousand lenses, according to the insect, register only form and movement, in most cases.

How far an insect sees varies considerably. Unlike other eyes, the density and curvature of the lens remains constant. Butterflies, which are descended from the caddis fly, are believed to be the most far-sighted, with a range of about nine feet, whereas bumblebees and wasps—which, together with the ants, are the "brainiest" among insects— can see only two feet away. A praying mantis, hidden among the leaves of a windowbox, will show no sign of recognizing menacing gestures made within the room, but if a person leans out over the windowbox, the mantis will turn its head so that the eyes look up to and follow the movements of the great unknown shape looming above it.

The limited vision of insects is aided, in the search among flowers, by scent and color, although mistakes are frequently made and rectified only within the visual range of the insects—which may explain why they sometimes seem to be flitting from blossom to blossom without any practical reason.

Especially fascinating, among insects, are the "false" eyes which a number of them display, apparently for defense. Some moths and butterflies have markings on their wings, particularly the hind ones, which look like imitation eyes. Darwin decided that they are to deflect the attacks of birds, whose target in hunting is usually the eyes of their victims or close behind them. This camouflage protects the vital parts of the insect, and even if the hind wings are torn flight is still possible by means of the front pair.

The spectacular calico butterfly has hind wings marked and colored like the face and eyes of the owl, and often alights upside down, so that the "owl-head" and "eyes" appear in the proper position to frighten or deceive enemies.

The North American polyphemus moth, ranging from coast to coast and south into Mexico, has on each of its four large wings an oval "window," so transparent that it is possible to see the smallest details through them. On the back wings, these transparencies are circled by bands of blue and black, giving an illusion of huge staring eyes.

The caterpillar of the sphinx moth has only a few, almost invisible simple eyes, the compound eyes of the adult having not yet formed, but when attacked by birds it makes a squeaking protest, at the same time raising its tail to show a distinctly eyelike bulge, which it moves rapidly to and fro until the frightened birds give up.

The larva of the tiger swallowtail has eye markings on it, too. In describing these imitation eyes, Edwin Way Teale in *Grassroot Jungles* (New York: Dodd, Mead and Company, 1945), adds that, when at rest, the swallowtail caterpillars "expand part of their bodies so that they resemble the heads of green snakes with yellow eyes, and birds sometimes retreat in screaming alarm when they come upon these false faces among the leaves."

The habits of some insects are affected by their eyes. There is a certain kind of katydid, for example, that has one tune for the daytime and another for night. Should a shadow chance to fall, masking off the light, the katydid will immediately change its tune to that of night.

Then again, some insects' eyes are affected by their habits. The menacing, sparkling eyes of spiders (not considered true insects because they have eight legs—two too many) can number from two to eight; the striped jumping-spider has four set in a row. All spiders' eyes are placed in the position most suitable for use according to each one's special kind of hideout. The daddy longlegs, also an eight-legged creature like the spider, has its eyes set in a sort of hump on its back, and looks between its towering knees as it walks.

A few insects are little affected by their eyes. An ant, for one, uses its antennae more than its eyes to carry on its almost human ordering of life. If its eyes are waxed over so as to exclude sight, it continues its social activities with little or no disturbance. It is only when damage is done to its antennae that it is lost.

Sex can make a difference in the size of insect eyes. One example is the drone, or male hive bee, whose eyes are larger than those of the female. The increase in size is almost all in the upper part, and is thought to be related to the pairing of bees high in the air, which makes it necessary for the drone to look upward in search of its mate.

Perhaps the most curious of all insect eyes are those of the dragonfly. This glittering, colorful child of the sun has not altered greatly, either in structure or habits, since its origin millions of years ago. While almost everything around it changed and became more and more complex, the dragonfly remained content to have just its primitive needs supplied—sunshine, and insects pleasing to its taste. It suffers no prolonged old age, for, with its young nymphs safely cradled beneath the water, it gives in to the first intense cold of autumn. Almost until its last few moments of life it is tremendously active, breathing a hundred and eighteen times a minute, very much faster than man, and darting above the ponds, rising, falling, hovering, sometimes flying at speeds around sixty miles an hour.

This pioneer among insects—probably the first to fly—

perfected a form of "double vision" ages and ages before Benjamin Franklin invented bifocal spectacles. Its enormous compound eyes, usually set so that they almost touch one another, are composed of about thirty thousand lenses in each one of the pair. Every second or third of the retinal light-sensitive cells has its own minute lens, so that not only the cells form a mosaic picture of the object regarded by the insect, but the little lenses do as well—which seems a horribly complicated way to see things, but does not appear to worry the dragonfly unduly. In some types, the lenses of the upper surface are twice as large as those below, and it is believed by some that the upper part of the eye registers movement and the lower stationary objects. The dragonfly's head is like half of a hollow ball. It works on a ball-and-socket arrangement that enables the insect to turn its head almost completely around and, in spite of its actual eyes' being static, see below and above. Among all the flying invertebrates, the extraordinarily active and predatory dragonfly alone needs such complex eyes.

Probably it was the change in environment, the increasingly dense growth of jungle and forest around them that stimulated primitive reptiles to leap from branch to branch and slowly become birds—"glorified reptiles," as Julian Huxley called them. Many ages and many stages of evolution were to pass before the change from saurian to avian form was complete. We are not sure whether feathers came into being before the blood became warm, or whether it was the other way around, but in any case the scales of the ancestral form, probably an arboreal reptile, became tubular and fringed, gradually covering parts of the body of a hopping, tree-loving animal with down.

In time, this down became feathers, neatly laid one upon another, like scales, along the back, tail, thighs, and "forearms." Feathers are the strongest structures, for their size and weight, known to nature. The first birdlike creature could hop or walk on two legs, and used its forearms for pulling, clinging, and climbing. As its feathers gradually spread all over its body, and increased in size, it was able to take long leaps among the trees and canes and ferns, and finally to glide on air currents between the branches. Its feather-borne flight was a great improvement on that of the skin-planed pterodactyls, although at first the "fingers" of its forearms, or wings, were too free, the bones too delicate, and the important "wishbone" (sternum) of the breast was absent or too small for flight. Time took care of all these faults, and when they were remedied the creature became the first true bird—the archeopteryx, or "ancient flyer."

Men have always envied the birds as they soar alone in beauty through the skies, or wheel in great flocks on their way to better lands, but man has a great gift which the bird lacks—hands. In giving up its hands, in allowing its fingers to fuse together into wing parts so that it might achieve perfection in flight, which stimulated the finest known visual sense, a bird has gained much but lost more. We are ahead of the birds, in that their brains have not developed along with their vision, and our brains have surpassed our eyes.

Birds have made two especially important contributions to the story of eyes. They have perfected their fovea far beyond those of lizards and men, and some have moved their eyes from the sides to the front of their heads. These two achievements are closely connected.

Frontal eyes are found in all hunting types of animals— where acute sight for spotting and pouncing on prey is the most important sense—but they are not found among the hunted, who must have a wide field of vision to anticipate their enemies. The fox looks forward, but the rabbit looks sideways; the owl forward, but the mouse to the sides; the cat forward, but the pigeon sideways; and so on.

Although birds' eyes are essentially reptilian, they surpass those of any mammal in sharpness of vision, power, and rapidity of accommodation. They are so large—only a small portion is visible outside the head—that they have taken up most of the room in the skull, with the result that the brain is very small (hence the popular expression, "bird-brained").

The eyeball of a bird, instead of being globular, is tubular, like a stubby telescope. At the front and back of it are the bony, overlapping sclerotic plates. In young birds the iris at first is a rather dull brown color, but as the bird grows up the iris, in many cases, becomes attractively colored, an important asset during the mating season, for birds actually "make eyes" at one another. The pupil of the eye is rounded, except in fowls where it is oval. The retina is composed almost entirely of cones, for most birds fly during the daytime and roost at night. The tips of the cones are coated with red or yellow oil droplets, as they were in some of their remote ancestors, which filter the light much as sunglasses do.

Like lizards, birds have a third eyelid, the nictitating membrane, but in an improved version, motivated by more than one distinct muscle. Of their two outer lids, only the lower is movable, and eyelashes, which are nothing more than feathers without barbs, appear around the rims of the eyes in such birds as the ostrich and the Amazon parrots. These lashes are particularly useful to creatures who, like the ostrich, live in dry desert regions where the sand is frequently blown into their eyes. (Camels have thick, sweeping eyelashes that most women would covet.)

All birds have a *fovea centralis*—that wonderful concentration of centrally-placed retinal cells which makes it possible for an eye to be aimed—and in many kinds, like the swallows, there is a second fovea toward the posterior or outer region. The bird's eye usually is directed to the side, and the central fovea is aimed at this side visual field.

Vision straight ahead is important to a bird in flight, however, and the second fovea gives each eye a perception of
detail in the forward part of each visual field.

Other birds improve even on this wide range of vision,
their fovea being spread in a strip right across the retina,
bringing a very extensive strip of the landscape into
sharp focus.

Again, it is obvious from the arrangement of their retinal
cells that visual acuity in birds is very fine, the cells in
small birds in particular being set much closer together
than ours, essential to the discovery of small food seeds.
Nocturnal birds, such as the owl or the nightingale, show
no signs of night-blindness as we do, their retinas being
composed mostly of rods, collected in larger groups than
ours. The piercing eyesight of hawks, which can spot their
tiny, half-hidden prey from an incredible height, is· well
known. It has been mentioned in a previous chapter that
the color sense of birds is very likely wider than our own.
All this adds up to the fact that in birds vision is of the first
importance—after the proprioceptive sense.

You may not know this sense by its long name, yet we
all have it, to a greater or lesser degree. It is a sixth sense,
and extremely valuable, for without it neither the birds nor
you and I could make a proper move. It is the sense of
position or movement of the body in space. It is closely
connected with balance. If you are sitting in a theater,
and the lights go out suddenly, leaving you completely in

the dark, you are still aware of where every part of you is; you do not have to move a leg or hand to find this out. Without this sense you would not be aware of whether or not your knees were bent or your body upright or seated, but fortunately you have it—fortunately, because it is obvious that without it you would not know what move to make first in getting up or walking. We take this knowledge for granted, but if we really concentrate our thoughts we can feel this sensing going on just below the level of our everyday attention, and it can be improved by practice.

The proprioceptive sense in birds makes up considerably for their lack of brain power, and the consequent possible loss of some of the things offered them by their splendid eyes. In some birds the eyes weigh more than the brain, in others each eye does. That part of the brain which is concerned with vision takes up most of the bulk of the entire brain. The surface of the brain is mostly quite smooth, without convolutions, although a slight furrow appears in pigeons, fowls, and birds of prey.

Birds can work out their positions in geographic space; and they probably know whether or not it is nearing the time to sleep, or the hour when the tide is low or high, or the day when they should be preparing to migrate, by looking at the sun slant. Shipwrecked men far out at sea, in small boats without compasses, have used birds to guide them to land. The proprioceptive messages from the muscles which move and focus the eyes help the birds in making rapid judgments of distance and quick changes of direction.

Patient watchers of birds, who have really become intimate with their every sensitive motion and expression, are familiar with the extraordinary "telepathy" that exists between them. Just as some groups of musicians play perfectly together without a conductor, not merely because they have rehearsed endlessly, but because their "sixth sense" pulls each individual's spirit, technique, and delight in the music into one exquisite flow of sound, so do flocks of migrating birds come together, wheel one way and then the other in perfect unison, and finally, without any apparent signal from any one of them, flow away together beyond the horizon.

Chapter 8

NIGHT, DAY, AND 3-D

Frontal, highly developed eyes with stereoscopic vision, as well as active brains, appear in most animals closely related to man.

At the top of the picture opposite is a lemur; below it, to the left, is a little tarsier; to the right, a baboon; below the baboon, a chimpanzee and a huge gorilla.

Through peace and war, the great wheel of time turns steadily through light and dark.
—Donald Culross Peattie

W E HUMANS, generally speaking, like to be up and about in the daytime and go to bed at night. If we were asked why, we probably would consider the question rather silly, but if pressed we might reply that of course we like to be awake in the daytime because everything seems so nice and safe in the light of the sun, it feels good to be out in it, and we can see so much better—and, anyway, everybody *does.* . . .

Nights can be beautiful, too, yet most of us are in the habit of pursuing our daily bread and some recreation in the daytime. How many of us really think this through, and wonder *why?*

An explanation may strike us as we trace back to the habits of creatures living not so long, comparatively speaking, after the wheel of time first began to turn on earth. Among the lowest of a certain kind of placental mammal— the primates—are small animals with sharp, foxlike muzzles, large eyes, and very soft woolly fur, called lemuroids. In them, and up through the highest type of mammal, a

gradual change can be traced from the nocturnal habits of
their ancient insect-eating ancestors to the diurnal habits
of some monkeys, and men.

Ever since that moment when the first watery sunbeam
lanced through primeval darkness in promise to the sea,
day has unfailingly followed night in at least seven hundred and thirty billion cycles. During this astronomical
number of times that light intensity has varied from dark
to bright, the amount that has fallen upon living eyes has
had an important effect upon their evolution, and consequently upon the habits of their owners, particularly those
milk-giving animals of which man is one.

A few years ago (1955), a new fossil was found by members of the American Museum of Natural History in a mile-
high Arizona desert. It was the fossil of a cat-sized creature
that lived millions of years ago in the swamps. This may
be the "missing link" between reptiles and mammals. Its
eye sockets were large, and its jaw was similar to that of a
reptile, but the teeth classified it as a mammal. In other
words, it was "half and half." It has been named *Tritylodon*
(three-cusp-toothed), and similar finds have been made
in South Africa, southern England, and southwest China.
It is possible that the tritylodon spent much of its time up
in the eternal twilight of the tangle of great ferns and canebrakes. After about thirty million years of life, it became
extinct, supplanted by true mammals.

There are three kinds of mammals—the egg-laying

monotremes, extinct now except for the duck-billed platypus and certain kinds of anteaters; the pouched marsupials, like the opossum and the comparative newcomer kangaroo; and the milk-giving placentals, who bear their young alive. The eyes of the monotremes and the marsupials are mostly like those of the reptiles, but the placental eye is entirely distinct. It is more like that of an amphibian, possibly because the first placentals lived a nocturnal life, depending largely upon senses other than visual.

As time continued to perform its slow magic, the placentals, sometimes little more than a mouse in size, grew as large as a goat and larger, but in the immediate step following their first stage they resembled, more than anything, a creature living today, named *Tarsier spectralis.*

The tarsier looks like something out of an early Victorian children's tale of sprites and hobgoblins. It can fit into the palm of your hand, gripping tightly onto your fingers with its curious, naked little hands and feet, which are divided into long, blunt-tipped "fingers" and "toes" like tiny flat spoons. It has a thin tail longer than its small, furred body, with a sort of plume like a paint brush at the end. Its head is large, with alert, rounded ears and a puckish smile. Its huge, slightly bulging round eyes stare brightly. Most lemur retinas contain both rods and cones, although they have no color sense, but the tarsier retina is made up purely of nocturnal rods.

From the earliest stage of its development, the eye of
the unborn placental mammal is much smaller in relation
to the head than that of a bird, and even when fully grown
is smaller compared to the size of the body than in any
other animal. Before the baby mammal is born, there are
many seemingly unnecessary defects about its eye. For one
thing, the vitreous—that clear, colorless jelly which fills the
back part of the eyeball—is full of tiny blood vessels, and
although these disappear at birth, often a few bits of them
are left floating about over the lens, and only through habit
does the animal become unaware of them. In kittens and
puppies, this shriveling of the blood vessels is not complete
until about ten days after birth, when the eyes finally open.
For another thing, the mammalian lens is not so well developed or elastic as that of a bird, and before birth it, too,
is masked with blood vessels which later more or less dis-
perse. The lens in monkey and man is flattened, with no
more curve than a good magnifying glass; however, it is
not true, as some believe, that eyes can magnify—that the
bigger the animal's eye the more enormous and fearsome
things appear to it. Look into any eye, and you will see
that the picture reflected in it is much smaller than reality.
The actual size of objects seen is a matter of past experience coupled with touch. A horse's eyes are large and
prominently placed not to magnify objects but to enable
the horse to see almost all around without turning his

head. (A hare sees in the same way, for another example.) This all-inclusive visual field is necessary to the horse so that it can perceive the approach from any direction of its natural enemy, the wolf, and kick out against it. Blinkers are put at the sides of some horses' eyes to mask off most of the visual field, concentrating the horses' attention on what lies ahead.

The lids and lubricants of most mammalian eyes are much the same as ours. One remarkable exception is the rhinoceros, which does not blink its lids to lubricate and cleanse its eyes, but every now and then pulls the eyes deep into their sockets, whirls them around a bit, then slips them back into place. A few mammals have functioning third eyelids—nictitating membranes—which protect their eyes when traveling through sandy areas or thick underbrush. Polar bears have slightly transparent ones, which protect their eyes from snow glare.

Being mostly nocturnal, the lower mammals had little need for accommodation in their eyes, and the ciliary, or focusing muscle, is lacking in the monotremes, although a small one still exists in the marsupials, but of inferior structure. The same thing happened to the sphincter, or constricting muscle of the pupil. In the higher mammals, including man, both these muscles have lost their striated, or grooved, formation which, where it exists, enables the muscles to work more rapidly. Here again, the bird's eye is superior to our own, their muscles being striated in order that the eye may accommodate itself in keeping with the demands of swift flight.

The early tarsier-type primate was warm-blooded, with a more active body chemistry than any other living thing before it. It had a highly sensitive nervous system, and a more adaptive brain. It developed better vision than any other mammal living at that time, because within the green limits of its home in the trees—dim-lit, narrow, but safe— sight became more important than any other of the senses. This excellent eyesight helped to stimulate that part of the brain where visual impressions are received until it dominated over all the rest, and because of this, together with the little creature's astonishing ability to walk on its hind legs and grip firmly with its "hands," encouraged the growth of another part of the brain, that which controls the sense of touch and of muscular effort.

From these two developments came full *attention,* a big step on the way to reflective thought. The tiny tarsier was fully aware that down below, away from the trees in the unfiltered light of day, lay danger. It knew that it should not hunt its food under such conditions, because its small size alone made it vulnerable to attack from enemies. Down there on the ground, its keen eyesight would not help it so much as would a sense of scent, or ears cocked to the slightest hint of menacing sound, or hackles that rose when danger loomed, all of which, to a considerable degree, it lacked. Its brain was changing from a crude "scenting" brain to a sophisticated "sight" one. In the constant struggle for existence, it habitually took advantage of the night and the treetops.

Those nights were full of mystery and strange sights. If there happened to be much starlight, or a bright moon, the light they shed would often be reflected in a pair of waiting eyes, hidden in the vegetation.

All eyes that glow blue or green in the dark—those of the cat family, some dogs, sheep, oxen, for instance—do so because of a marvelous concave reflector behind the transparent retina, called the *tapetum lucidum*. Contrary to popular and poetical belief, these eyes do not shine of their own accord, but simply reflect strongly any available light much as does a metal reflector behind an old-fashioned lamp, thus greatly improving their owner's nocturnal vision. If this tapetum cannot be shut off from the light, and if it is connected with a retina without a protectingly narrow, slit-type pupil, like that of the cat or opossum, then the animal cannot get along in dazzling daylight.

Those animals whose habits make it necessary for them to see a little during parts of the day and night, or whose eye formation is such as to have turned their habits into part-day and part-night ones, see by combining in their eyes certain adaptations for both strong and weak light, such as a suitably balanced number of rods and cones. Actually, if you stop to think about it, it can be realized that an eye specialized for twenty-four-hour vision would be quite unsuccessful, because it could function properly only during the brief periods of morning, or evening, twilight.

The closest approach to "intermediate" or *arrhythmic* twenty-four-hour vision occurs in the hoofed mammals, in animals such as elephants, or in bears and wolves. Their retinas and pupils are relatively static, and their entire eyes and retinal images are large, with a suitable distribution of rods and cones, aided by that tapetum otherwise usually associated with nocturnal creatures. Although this vision tends to be short-sighted, in many cases it is good enough, both night and day, for these animals to depend on it for stalking and pouncing on their prey at close quarters, having first picked up the trail at long range through hearing and scent.

A different kind of animal, the lemur, nevertheless shares common ancestry with the tarsier. The lemur retina contains both rods and cones, and is adapted to a more diurnal mode of life, but those which have been examined for color vision have been found wanting. A fovea does not exist in the lemur eye, and it is believed that none of the breed has any power of accommodation either.

After the lemurs and tarsiers came the real monkeys, the baboons, and the apes. As they appeared, increased all over the world, and grew larger, their vision improved more and more. (This advantage led, in another sense, to a disadvantage. The power of smell became less, because it was less used.) The monkeys' brains developed considerably and with the increase in the size of the brain case the bony structure of their faces decreased in size until finally there remained no noticeable obstruction between the two eyes, set squarely on the top front of their heads. This resulted in the overlapping of the two fields of vision in the eyes, with much improved stereoscopic vision—relief and perspective.

Perfect binocular sight followed the now exactly parallel axes of the eye, and the eyeball moved in response to the monkey's will, aiming the somewhat shallow but adequate fovea which grew close to the axis of the eye. Color vision appeared for at least the fifth time in vertebrate history and a completely new power of accommodation evolved by which the eye could either adjust for viewing objects clearly from distances of several feet down to just an inch or two, or become set for objects from several feet away to infinity.

Because of their quick brains and their amazing agility in escaping from enemies, the first monkeys and apes were not afraid to make constant trips down to earth, even though at first their large eyes were not used to bright sunlight, and they could not see behind them. Gradually they became more and more diurnal in their habits, their retinas grew rich in cones (although these were simple in structure compared to those of their ancestors), and their eyes, originally large in keeping with their previous nocturnal life among the leaves, grew smaller. The fovea and the retinal region around it were full of a yellow pigment. Together these yellow areas replaced the important but long-lost oil droplets of the more primitive animals.

And then some of those early monkeys left the trees—or rather, the trees left them. The climate had become drier and much colder, and the great forests which had flourished over almost all the world shrank into small woods and clumps, particularly in the temperate zones. Therefore it is believed that it was in these zones the simians first came down to earth to stay.

To begin with, they walked bent over like old men, swinging their long arms, or occasionally supporting the weight of their body on the backs of their hands which rested on the ground. Their excellent eyesight enabled them to pick out very small food or other objects, which they turned over and over in their increasingly sensitive hands, examining them with growing curiosity.

Then, about a million years ago, one of the greatest changes in evolution in the direction of man took place. Among the simians living at that time, some happened to be born with a shorter pelvis. The thigh muscles attached to this bone were affected, and the ability to finish each step with a drive—the human way of walking—arrived. The new position of the pelvis brought about a more erect position of the body and freed the arms and hands, so that the picking up of objects of interest, the close scrutiny of them by the splendid eyes, became a habit, increasing the powers of observation and deduction. Thus it was that the simians became entirely diurnal in their habits, sleeping at night in sheltered crannies between rocks or holes in the cliffs, where prowling enemies could not reach them.

The ability of the carnivores to see and kill at night is said to be the explanation for our own primitive fear of the dark. Once, long, long ago, we hunted by day, but at night, naked and half-blind, we were the hunted.

And so, standing bravely erect for the first time, instead of constantly looking downward from dim hideaways in the trees, man's immediate ancestor began to look up with the light of reason dawning in his eyes.

Chapter 9

THE HUMAN EYE

A primitive man, his vision probably superior to ours, looks at a tree. The image of the tree is received upside down by the eye, but is reversed to its proper position by the brain.

Above him, right (all ages are estimated):

A. A human embryo, twenty-eight days old, showing optic vesicle in early stage.

B. Thirty-two-day-old human embryo with lens placode, an area of thickened membrane overlying the optic vesicle.

C. The embryo at thirty-seven days. The dark line under the optic vesicle is the rudimentary jaw passing forward and fusing with the nasal fold.

D. At the age of forty-six days, the eyelid outline is clearly defined.

E. The human embryo at sixty days, showing further development of the eyelids, which are fused. (They open at about the seventh month.)

Above, left:

1. The optic stalk and section of optic cup, containing the lens vesicle, in a human embryo estimated at thirty-seven days.

2. The optic cup at an estimated age of forty days, filled with rudimentary vitreous humor, and showing the developing lens with covering corneal membrane.

3. Human embryo eye at the third month, showing fused eyelids and iris formation.

4. Section of further developed eye of human embryo, showing differentiation of the parts of the retina and growth of the iris.

5. Posterior half of the wall of the eyeball, showing blood vessels branching from the retinal artery and vein, which enter and leave the eye, respectively, in the axis of the optic nerve. Central black dot is the optic disc.

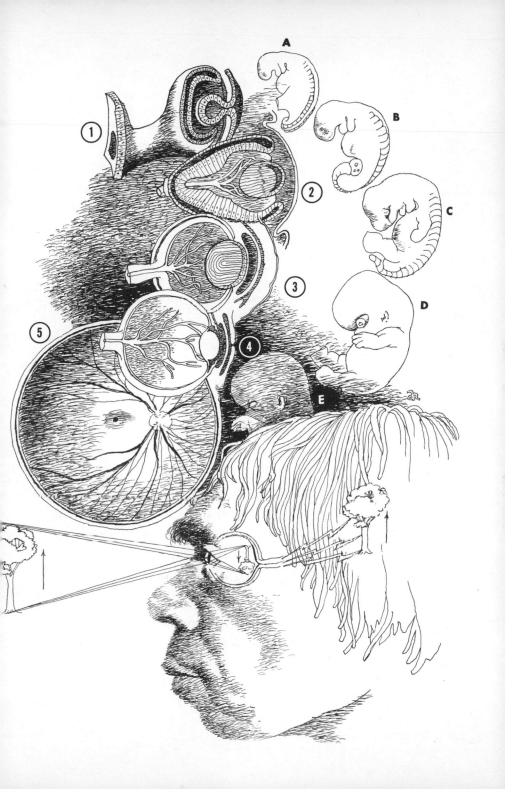

I gazed—and gazed—but little thought
What wealth the show to me had brought . . .
—William Wordsworth, "The Daffodils"

THE LITTLE hairy man, clad in an animal skin, looked steadily at the night sky framed by the entrance to his cave, then turned to the picture he was painting on the wall. He was putting in certain stars among the many he saw—stars visible to us now, as we gaze upward with our inferior eyesight, only through the aid of telescopes.

The urge to continue his work had awakened the caveman early, and now he was racing against time. Soon the stars would fade from sight before the rising sun. He painted by the fitful yellow light of a crude oil lamp, the evil smell from which mingled with other heavy odors in the cave. Its light flickered over the crouched forms of his two assistants, younger men who were grinding up the earth colors for him. He and they had achieved their ability to handle their tools possibly because an earlier animal, similar to the near-human creature named *Australopithecus,* had walked erect, with frontal eyes beneath an arched brow. Even though that animal's elbows did not

flex as easily as the men's did, the new posture brought
about the release of hands, eyes, and brain for a wider use
than locomotion, feeding, and defense, and in time led to
the understanding and use of tools. In different parts of the
world, the varying amounts of sunshine, and the ultraviolet rays reaching primitive man's body from it, deter-
mined the growth of his brain, and consequently his
thoughts and culture.

In the middle of the cave, below a funnel-shaped cleft
in the roof at the top of which one horn of a new moon
showed, a heavily pregnant woman was cooking meat on
a stick over a small fire. Huddled close to the fire was an
aged, half-blind man, the artist's father, patiently awaiting
his food. His blind helplessness had made him unwanted
and neglected by the others, and he lived out each day in
misery and apprehension. Beside him squatted one of his
daughters, picking through the hair of a small, impatient
boy trapped between her raised knees.

The older people about the boy were not much more
advanced mentally than he. From the beginning, man
sensed first and thought afterward. When the artist caveman put in certain lines and deeper, shadowy colors about
his animals on the wall, nobody in the cave laughed when
the boy went up to the painting and tried to grasp the leg
of one animal. They, too, saw the three-dimensional effect
of the painting, and sympathized with the boy when he
felt cheated at finding no round limb to take hold of. Even

today, a few among the natives of a remote part of an island in the Pacific have been known to walk around the back of a painter's easel, looking for the other side of the face on the canvas. The people in that primitive cave felt themselves superior to the beasts they fought and hunted, but, apart from the wall paintings, they thought about little more than how to avoid hunger, thirst, and cold. They watched for food, they listened to the life-giving stream rushing over the rocks, and, even over the smell of cooked meat, they knew the freshness of the pine trees that gave them fuel. They cowered, now, at a sudden flash of lightning and the following peal of thunder, wondering fearfully about it, but at the coming of the rain some of them went outside, stretching and turning up their faces and the palms of their hands to it.

At a second roll of thunder, louder than the first, the pregnant woman handed her stick of meat to the other and went to the rear of the cave. There she lay down, whimpering a little. The other woman finished the cooking, bit off a large chunk of the juicy flesh, and gave the rest to the men. After a while, still chewing strongly, she went to look at the other woman, who had become quiet. Beside her, on the stone floor, lay her newborn infant, a baby girl.

A little of the story of evolution had been repeated by that baby during the nine months she had rested in her mother's womb, starting with a minute "egg," developing to the embryo fish stage, even including gills, and then on to the infant mammal. The formation of the eyes was no less amazing. Followed step by step, the mystery of our own eyes unfolds.

In that unborn child, from the miraculous combination of protein, sugar, fat, salts, and eighty per cent water of which an eye is made, there came a bud of multiplying granular skin cells. The bud was less than one ten-thousandth part of the size of a mature eye, and it grew in layers to form, first, a cornea, that transparent "window" in the center of the normally visible part of the coat of the eyeball.

Next, the cornea sank backward at its center to form a little sac, or capsule, which was then "pinched off" to become a detached, glass-clear lens, hung by a ligament just behind where the pupil of the iris would be, and directly in the path by which light would enter the eye after birth.

The lens grew carefully until it was optically just right, with its two surfaces, front and back, truly centered on its axis, and curved to the exact degree to ensure proper light focus on the sensitive retina, which later would make its appearance at the rear of the eye. This curvature of the lens would be controlled, as the child grew older, to accommodate for near or distant objects, through muscular tension and the elasticity of the thin lens capsule—a relatively weak power of accommodation compared to the efficient ciliary muscle of the reptile. The human lens is capable of bulging itself to conform, roughly, to the various sizes of the pupil under different light exposures, bringing into focus objects from twenty feet away down to a few inches. When the bulge relaxes, the eye is set for objects from twenty feet away to infinity.

Meanwhile, some of the skin cells from around the eye of the unborn babe combined into a ball—fibrous, white, opaque—set in the optic cup, or socket, and called the sclera. The thin, moist, flexible skin of the sclera, the con-junctiva, contains a few blood vessels, which can be plainly seen if our eyes become irritated, when the blood vessel dilate, filling with more blood, and cause what we call a "bloodshot" condition.

The new baby's eyeball was separated into two parts by the lens—a small front section and a larger back, both filled with a watery substance kept at a certain pressure by an astounding system of minute valves. This maintains the shape of the eyeball, which otherwise would collapse into a limp mass of tissue. The fluid in the front chamber, between the cornea and the lens, is known as the aqueous humor, and that in the back chamber, of a more jelly-like consistency, is called the vitreous.

There are little bits and strings of cells in our vitreous left from the blood vessels which were present before birth. If we look up at a clear sky, or the colorless sheet of a fog, we become aware of these little floaters, and as our age increases the specks may change their position and make us aware of them for the first time. This is nothing to worry about. The floaters are as much part of our anatomy as anything else.

The outer surface of the cornea, where it is exposed to the world, is constantly washed over by tear-water, which has the power of killing germs. The cleansing tear-water is made by what is known as the lachrymal apparatus, which consists of a tear gland over the outer corner of the eye, under the bony eyebrow ridge; the ducts which carry this gland's teary secretion to the upper eyelid; and the two canals below the eye by which the tears are carried off after their work on the surface of the cornea, so that they do not constantly run down over the cheeks. These canal apertures run inward into a tear sac, and from there through a duct into the nasal chamber, which is why we have to blow our nose when we cry. If our eyes were not constantly washed this way, they would dry up and we would lose our vision.

The vital core of sight, the light-sensitive retinal "screen," was meanwhile growing around about three-quarters of the eye's vitreous chamber. When it reached the other quarter, at the beginning of the aqueous chamber, it separated from the body of the eyeball and turned in over the lens, ending in a circular, free border which, because of its attractive coloring, is called the iris. The free border gathered up around a retractile opening, the pupil.

The fibers of the iris are pigmented as an increased protection against light. The back of the iris is heavily colored a dark brown, while the front part, at least in the white races, is comparatively free from pigmentation at birth. As this front part of the iris is very transparent, and absorbs the long red and yellow light waves as they pass through it, the light reflected from the inner brown pigmentation looks blue, exactly as veins do through a delicate skin. This condition often remains throughout life, resulting in a blue-eyed person. Many people develop a rich, golden-brown pigment on the iris, and are brown-eyed, but if the layer is thin or spotty the iris is hazel in color, gray, or flecked. No two irises ever have quite the same pattern, and Bertillon, the fingerprint expert, suggested this fact be utilized in identifying criminals. (However, fingerprints have become the standard method, in spite of the possibility of altering fingertips through plastic surgery.)

The color of eyes is controlled by numerous genes, and a study of their heredity is not easy. Many old wives' tales have recently been disproved, though; it is not true, for instance, that dark eye color is always more prevalent than light, and that the children of two blue-eyed parents cannot have brown eyes, although this happens rarely.

After birth, the pupil, or hole in the baby's iris, would be automatically expanded or contracted by the different amounts of light reflected from the objects observed. The muscles of the iris are the only muscles in the human body that are in themselves photosensitive—that is, capable of reacting to light.

The retina originally grew outward from the brain, so consequently it is built in much the same way as the brain. There are photosensitive layers of cells that break down the images of the external world into numerous minute dots, which again are transformed into electrical currents by a means as yet little understood, and then they are dispatched over the optic nerve to the brain.

If you throw a beam of light, say from a strong flashlight, into someone's eye through the pupil, and examine the retina with a magnifying glass, you will see it there, glowing red behind the lens. Probably the next thing you will notice about the retina will be the optic disc, a round or oval spot about 1.55 millimeters in diameter, at the entrance to the optic nerve. From this spot, the brilliant red retinal vessels ray out like the spokes of a fine wire wheel, dividing countlessly as they go. The central optic pit, or fovea, shows as a yellowish spot, not far from the optic disc, in which all the cells are cones. From this fovea—the central "aiming" point of the eye—out into the rest of the retina, the cones become fewer and fewer, giving place to rods, until on the periphery there are only rods. Man has grown a double eye—the central fovea of cones, which is a daylight image and color "focuser," and a peripheral rod eye, which is a twilight "finder." The entire retina, viewed in this special way with light and magnifier, is a fascinatingly beautiful work of nature.

So it is that, with our double eye, we see two worlds—a

brightly colored daylight world with a highly detailed central point, and a colorless moonlight one without any central point, yet with a clear over-all perception of movement and shadows. Scientists are constanly searching for ways to improve our night vision, of particular importance to night fliers. Dr. Toshimasa Hanaoka, of Nara Women's University in Japan, has announced in *Nature* magazine that a hormone secreted by the pituitary gland is an aid in adapting the eye to see in the dark. This hormone controls pigment formation, and injections under the skin of a highly purified fraction shorten the time required for vision to adapt to the dark.

The nerves connecting the retina with the brain are rather complex. There are about one hundred and thirty-seven million "seeing" elements on the human retina, but the number of nerve lines connecting them with the brain reduces to little more than a million. These work in relays, carefully shunting each light picture received to the right reception point in the brain by means of rhythmic streams of fleeting electrical impulses. The picture caught by the retina is only two-dimensional, like any other reproduction, and it remains for the brain to add the third dimension, and color.

Perhaps the most astonishing of all things about the retina—astonishing, at least, when first learned—is that it registers the world we look at upside down. You are not reading this page from top to bottom and left to right, but

from bottom to top and right to left. When you looked into
the retina with your special glass and light, you saw that
the optic disc at the entrance of the optic nerve was on the
left side of the fovea (the left of the retina, that is, not your
left). This is because the right side of the retina sees things
to the left, the top sees the ground, the left side sees
things to the right, and the bottom sees the sky. The reversal of the picture to the "proper" way up takes place
during the processing of the visual message by the brain,
without any conscious effort on our part.

In the brain, the eye messages first go to the optic
thalamus, where they are "developed" into meaning and
then sent on to the occipital lobe. There, the pyramidal
cells of the cerebral cortex become aware of them, with the
aid of optical memories stored in the "library" of the brain.
These marvelous mental files actually preserve everything
we ever see. If we do not always remember it all, it is not
because our recollection is at fault. Recollection is always
perfect, unless that part of the brain has been injured or
become diseased. Normally, *recollection* is there for the
tapping any time, but our power of remembering—our
memory, which motivates our recollection files—sometimes
fails us for such reasons as tiredness, sickness, or having
"too much on our mind." If all or any of these visual
archives in the brain are somehow destroyed, what is
known as memory blindness sets in, and the sense of touch
must be brought into play for recognition and re-filing of

all or certain objects, even though the eye aimed upon
them may be perfectly healthy in itself.

We do not always employ all of our store of knowledge.
In everyday life, most of us, with the possible exception
of some artists and poets, usually pay attention only to the
surface of things around us. It is only in dreams that occasionally we become aware of other elements, of deeper
meanings we had not consciously experienced when
awake. The extraordinary memory of Helen Keller, blind
and deaf from the age of nineteen months through an
attack of scarlet fever, enables her to recollect something
of what sunlight is like, although this does not enter her
dreams, so far as can be told, except through some obscure
combination of ideas difficult for most seeing people to
understand.

As time went on, the unborn cave baby's eyelids formed
from folds of skin strengthened by plates of fibrous tissue,
but to begin with they were tightly sealed. Six months
before birth, the eyes began to move slightly behind the
closed lids, but they had not yet learned coordination, and
moved independently of each other. Later, the edges of
the lids would become smooth, oiled for action by a line
of glands connected to tiny ducts, their openings along the
rim of the lids looking like a row of pin pricks.

In front of these oil ducts the eyelashes began to grow,
longer on the upper lid and carefully bent away from the

sensitive cornea—immensely important as a defense sieve against foreign bodies which might otherwise enter and injure the eye.

Above the lids, at the bony edge of the eye socket, came the eyebrows, thought by a few people to be the remains of the long, sensory whiskers which some lower animals have on their foreheads as warning devices, but useful to us now only in preventing perspiration from running into the eyes from the brow.

The final touch to the baby's eyes was a little dab of pink in the inner, nasal corner, a vestige of that once-working third lid, the nictitating membrane, and a constant reminder of our ancestry.

A week after her birth, the little girl lay on the floor of the cave with her head turned to one side, resting on her left arm. She was looking along the full length of this arm, seemingly fascinated by her own clenched fist. Her right arm was flexed at the shoulder and elbow, like the raised arm of a fencer in action, with the exception that this fist also was closed. She kept her hands closed because as yet she did not feel the need to use them, being content to take hold of her small world with her still very incomplete visual system. The light of the rising sun had opened her eyes, and her visual reflexes were responding to it. Reminiscent of the amoeba, she was seeing—perhaps sensing is the better word—with her entire being. She gazed in utter amazement, without understanding. We ourselves once in a while recapture that primitive bewilderment, at the moment of awakening in a strange room in which the furniture is unfamiliar and, for an instant, quite meaningless. Then our brain begins to work, and we orientate ourselves.

This the baby was learning to do. The position in which she lay was significant. During the first ten years of her life, at least, the cooperation between her eyes, hands, and brain would play a primary part in her development as an individual, just as it did in the evolution of the lower animals into human beings. She lay there, studying her hand long before she knew its use, getting accustomed to the look of it.

From the day she was born, her eyes had begun to work as a team—at first, a rather wobbly team. Now she fixed them briefly on a bright, beautiful object which her mother was playfully swinging to and fro close above her face. It was a gleaming ring of mother-of-pearl, suspended on a leather thong passed through a hole in the shell's center— her mother's treasured necklace.

As the shell swung like a pendulum from above the baby's right eye to her left, she closed her right eye and fixed her left on the necklace. As it swung back in the opposite direction, she reversed the action of her eyes. She continued to do this as long as her mother swung the necklace close to her eyes, but when the woman's attention was withdrawn to someone at the entrance of the cave, and she turned, moving the necklace away more than a foot, the baby opened both eyes in surprise and bewilderment. She could not focus at that distance. The pretty thing had disappeared.

The baby gave a howl, to attract her mother's attention back, but she did not cry. Man did not cry until he began to think. Crying is a comparatively new use for the cleansing tear-water. It is used as a reflex action when talking man finds that all logic, all powers of speech in the expression of emotion fail him. In the normal distribution of tears for cleansing and moistening purposes in the eye, the lids "suck" on the tear ducts and withdraw fluid every time they blink, which in many people is every two and a half seconds, in others less frequently. In that sense, we cry all day long, but tears that appear in such quantities as to overtax the drainage canals, overflow, and run down the cheeks are the result of spastically contracted facial muscles, due to emotion, which "accidentally" squeeze the tear glands. A Dutchman, learning English, once expressed this correctly by exclaiming about a comedian, "Ach! He made such fun I *laughed tears!*"

After about a month had passed, the baby's visual accommodation had improved. In her peculiar one-eye-at-a-time way, she could now see more distant objects. She followed quite rapidly the movements of people and animals about the cave, turning her head rhythmically from right to left and back again. After a little practice, she learned to team her eyes better, and about two months after her birth she was able to converge both eyes simultaneously upon her favorite objects.

At three months, her usual position was still with her head on one side, resting on her arm and looking along it as though her hand at the end of it was, after all, the most interesting thing in creation. However, at about the fourth month, she began to hold her head squarely in mid-position most of the time, bringing her hands symmetrically together over her stomach. She was about ready to take a steady look at life, and was avid for visual experience. She was launching on the experimental movements which to her fond parents appeared meaningless, or just simple play, but which were really vital in the development of her visual mental processes. Now and then her fingers would flex, as if in anticipation of the pleasures of touching and holding what she saw. Although she could not yet actually hold a thing, she stared intently at the objects on the cave floor, at the tree branches waving across the entrance, and the rough square blocks of stone around the hearth. Once in a while, she scratched the rock a little with her tiny fingernails.

Four weeks later, there was no doubt that she was picking up clearly with her eyes a small fragment of bone, not more than seven millimeters in diameter, which lay in shadow on the floor. The light color of the bone, of course, did make it appear larger than it was—merchants know this optical illusion, and often use it in selecting light-colored labels for their containers.

A great stride in the baby's perception came at seven months. Her small brother came to play with her, expecting little more from her than joy at being bounced up and down or when allowed to curl her hand around one of his little fingers. He sat beside her, and put down a piece of ivory tusk on which he had been trying to carve a picture. No sooner had he done so than his baby sister saw it, reached out her hand, and grasped it firmly. In triumph and delight, she immediately lifted the tusk to her mouth.

Finding the bone too large to get inside her mouth, she lowered it and threw it down with a twist of her wrist. She watched her own hand actions with astonished curiosity. She crawled over to retrieve the tusk, and brought it up to her face again for further investigation. As it came close up to her, her eyes converged upon it in order to focus, and she appeared to be squinting badly. The "squint" increased as a ray of light from the sinking sun fell on her eyes, causing her to screw them up tightly. But she was not really squinting. A true squint, commonly called a cast in the eye, is a condition in which one eye is considerably turned away or toward the other, and it is a physical fault.

Once again she threw the tusk away from her, her eyes diverging back to their normal central position as she watched her toy roll away for some distance. Then she picked up the tusk again and discovered a wonderful new game, passing the bone from hand to hand, back and forth, over and over again. She was duplicating with her hands the pendulum movement her eyes had used months earlier, when she had lain with clenched fists watching the shining shell.

That night, a little before dawn, the baby awoke and was vaguely aware that she wanted something. It was not only food, and she was warm enough. No, this was something else. She wanted her beloved tusk, but in the darkness it was impossible for her to see and find it. She set up a howl to attract attention to her need, and continued to complain, off and on, even though her mother fed her and did all she could to comfort her. It was not until dawn that the whimpering ceased, for then she *thought* she saw where her toy was.

By this time, however, everybody else in the cave had gone back to sleep, and there was no hand but her own to get the tusk. It did not look too far away to grasp, yet when she sleepily reached out for it she clutched nothing but air. Puzzled, she rubbed her eyes with her fists. They had misled her. They had told her this really was her nice, round, solid tusk, and not a chip or a piece of thin skin, but they had misjudged the distance.

While she was trying to solve this enormous problem, one of the family dogs came in from a hunting trip, and dropped a small dead animal near the tusk, between it and the baby. At the same time the sun rose, and painted a deep blue shadow along one edge of the tusk, outlining it clearly. The little dead animal overlapped part of the tusk, from the baby's viewpoint, and so showed it to be farther away than it had seemed at first.

The little girl was going through her first experience of something well known to her father, especially when he went out fishing in his rough skin coracle. Far from the shore, he would raise his eyes from the bone fishhook he was baiting, and diverge them in order to look homeward over the empty stretches of water. With no intervening objects between him and the shoreline on the horizon to give him the proper perspective, he would often under-estimate the distance. There were so many atmospheric currents and pathways between him and the landmarks, their outlines looked dim and their colors had faded to a hazy blue, saturated by space as the sky is on a fine day. On very clear mornings, they appeared much closer, but when there was no wind and the mist hung about, in the hazy twilight what glimpses he had of the shore seemed considerably farther away. The rough post to which he usually moored his coracle seemed never to have been, but when the sun finally broke through the mist and threw a dark shadow down one side of the post, there it was to be seen clearly, in all its promise of solid reality.

As he looked first one way, then the other, picking up familiar things as a clue to his position and distance from shore, the angle between near and far objects changed at his eyes. As he turned his head from side to side, the boat, although he was not paddling, seemed to move fairly rapidly in the opposite direction to the objects on shore. Those shore objects appeared to move only slightly in relation to the boat, and in the same direction his head was turning at the time. From these factors, his mind told him where he was, just as you can tell you are sitting at a table by a fifth-story window if you look over the windowsill and turn your head to look down at the houses to the left and right. Movie cartoonists have used this phenomenon of distant objects apparently moving more slowly and in the opposite direction to nearby ones, to give an illusion of depth in their landscapes.

In order to estimate distance, then, man must play his power of eye convergence slowly back and forth until it finds its dead center on the object; but the perception of solidity, or three-dimensions, is lightning fast, and has nothing to do with convergence. It is perceived by the brain.

The cave baby saw her tusk as a solid, three-dimensional object because it was so lighted by the sun as to have a shadowy side, which her brain recognized as relief on the tusk. Her left eye saw a little way round one side of the tusk, and her right eye a little way round the other side, but when each image fell upon exactly corresponding points in each retina the two views fused into one picture of a solid object. That experiment mentioned in the first chapter, of holding up your hand before your face and looking steadily "through" it at an object beyond, increased the number of your fingers because the right- and left-eyed images of them were not falling on the same points in your retinas. The images of whatever you were looking at beyond your hand were doing this. By simply looking at your fingers, instead of beyond them, you change your convergence and accommodation so that the images fall on the same points in both retinas, and the "extra" fingers slide into the proper number.

Employing this method, the small girl all alone was able to judge her proper distance from the object of her desire. It took her a little while to learn, but she did it. Crawling over the cave floor, she once more reached out her hand, and this time she touched and then grasped the tusk.

She was delighted at her success, and her eyes "lit up" with pleasure. This is often thought to be a figure of speech, but actually it is a fact. Research at the Yale Clinic of Child Development has shown that when the reflecting surface of a young child's retina is subjected to a beam of light from a retinoscope, the returning light varies not only in relation to certain different functionings of the eye, but with an increase of brightness when the infant identifies an object of interest. The cause of this is uncertain, for so far as I know there is as yet no device in general use among scientists that permits the study of the ultramicroscopic forces in the visual system.

However, light reflection is not the only reason for one person's having more "expressive" eyes than another. Expression in the eyes is due mostly to the movements of tiny facial muscles, and to the character lines in the skin that form around the eyes as the result of repeated use of these muscles in response to various emotions.

When the cave baby was about eleven months old, she became able to pick up neatly, with a precise action of fingers and thumb, the small white objects which five months before she had been able to grasp only with her eyes. As she continued to grow, her brain began to develop into a specialized organ of reason, and her visual actions became more and more symbolic. She had to associate visual experience with crude words; she had to learn what to do when she wanted to copy, with a stick in the sand, the vertical, horizontal, and curved lines her father painted on the cave wall, and perhaps add some of her own invention.

Her world was not static, as was that of her elders, but a plastic wonderland full of ever-increasing treasures. Her growing awareness of these exciting daily discoveries did not have to stop for her as long as she lived, unless she became lazy or too much attached to one aspect of life. There is more to see and enjoy and think about than we can possibly get into one lifetime, so every moment is precious.

The cave girl's eyes were perfect, but her brain was not

yet fully grown, so that her drawings were not particularly good. The fact that today some Johnnies can't read is due not necessarily to inferior eyesight or faulty tuition, but sometimes to a brain which is slow in developing, because it has not inherited all the right genes or received the right food. It has not the stimulus to "see" for itself, and it cannot be hurried. The ability to see well depends upon the *entire* animal.

Yet, if the cave child's eyes had not been good, if they had been attacked by any of the afflictions to which eyes are prone, there was nothing that could have been done about it. She would have had to suffer as did her grandfather, that neglected, half-blind old man. He was ignored by his own people, left to sit endlessly by the fire, groping for food and the few comforts at hand, because he could not see to work or hunt—and because nobody at that time had the remotest conception of the possibility of eyeglasses.

Chapter 10

A CONCISE HISTORY OF GLASSES

Here are some instruments invented by the brain of man to aid his own vision:

A. Convex lens.
B. Concave lens.
C. Early spectacles.
D. Modern horn-rimmed glasses.
E. Bifocal glasses.
F. Telescope.
G. Binoculars.
H. Compound microscope.

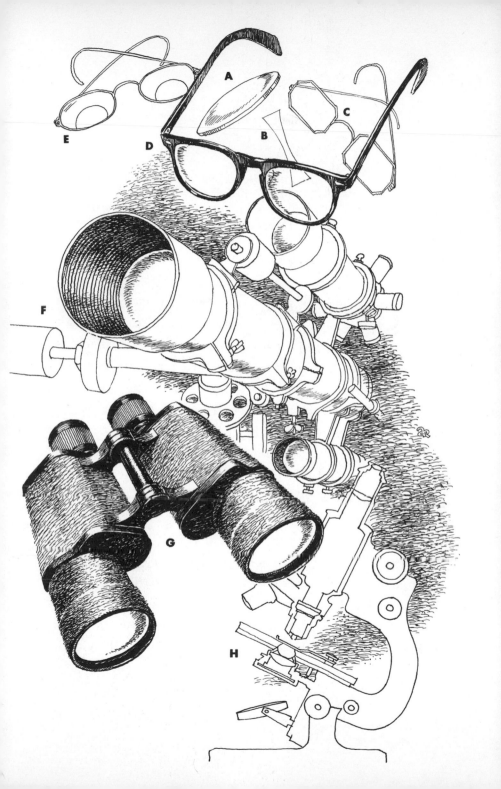

The universe is not to be narrowed down to the limits of understanding, which has been man's practice up to now, but the understanding must be stretched to take in the image of the universe as it is discovered.
—Francis Bacon

MANY ignorant people of the middle ages in Europe looked upon new inventions and discoveries with fear and superstition, considering them to be dangerous and evil works of magicians. Perhaps for this reason the early history of spectacles, which led to the telescope, and the microscope—man's contributions to the sense of sight—is shrouded in mystery.

The actual date of the invention of eyeglasses, and the name and nationality of their inventor, is uncertain, but long before the laws of optics were formulated the Chinese were wearing glasses.

Some scholars say that as early as 2283 B.C. a Chinese emperor used "lenses" made of rock crystal, quartz, topaz, or amethyst to observe the stars, but usually those ancients who suffered from inferior eyesight hired slaves to read to them. The first definite reference to glasses in the form familiar to us is in the writings of Confucius, about 500 B.C., where the sage claims to have relieved the eyes of a cobbler with a pair. But there is no hint that Confucius knew anything about the laws of refraction, the glasses simply being believed to possess medicinal properties. There is a record of a Chinese gentleman living during the Ming Dynasty (1368-1644) who gave a fine horse in exchange for a pair of glasses, and Marco Polo told that when he visited China in the 13th century the people were using "lenses," particularly old people, who employed them to decipher small print.

All kinds of reasons were given for the use of spectacles in those days—they indicated position, possessions, professions, intelligence, superstition, and even idiocy. The Chinese believed that a tortoise-shell frame would extend the normal period of life and bring good fortune—the tortoise being to them a sacred reptile—and sometimes these frames were worn without any glass in them. Chinese glasses were usually oval in shape, rather than round, and some of the frames were made of papier-mâché or horn. They were kept in place on the head either by strings that looped around the ears or by sidepieces pretty much like those in use today, and the nose-piece was often hinged in the center so that the glasses could be conveniently folded together into one.

The eventual invention of better aids to human vision was unwittingly delayed by the early Greek thinkers, who were averse to detailed experimental inquiry and who de-

voted their intellectual energies to philosophizing on the
nature of light itself. They neglected to pursue the study
of the refraction of light, although some glimmering of the
general principles of refraction and reflection, especially
in the images reflected in curved mirrors, comes into the
writings of Euclid (or, as some think, by a writer using his
name) in the third century B.C., but he was handicapped
by Plato's theory that vision emanates from the eye instead
of to it. Not until the beginning of the Christian era was
real progress made in the understanding of refraction,
when Cleomedes (ca. 50 A.D.) noticed the apparent bending of a stick partially submerged in water, and the fact
that a coin, placed in a basin which is then filled with
water, seems to rise.

The Emperor Nero had defective eyesight which he was
said to have aided by means of an emerald set in a ring,
but the jewel acted as a mirror, not as a lens. The lens, in
our sense of the word, was unknown to the ancients. However, strong glasses were often employed in those days for
burning. It has been recorded that burning glasses were
used to erase writings from wax tablets, or for setting fire
to enemy ships. Such usage is mentioned by the playwright
Aristophanes, who died about 385 B.C., and Pliny records
that burning glasses were used by physicians as cauteries.
It is thought possible that spheres of glass filled with water
were used as magnifiers by the gem cutters of antiquity,
and Seneca (who died around 63 A.D.) noticed that letters,

however small and dim, became comparatively large and distinct when seen through a water-filled globe.

Shortly before the first century A.D. the Phoenicians learned the ancient art of fine glass making from the Chinese, and Phoenician nitre merchants discovered that nitre mixed with sand became melted by the heat of the sun into glass. Some convex glass has been found in excavations at Pompeii and Nineveh, but the focal lengths of these glasses are so short that they cannot have been worn before the eyes.

Following the decadence of the Roman Empire and the suppression of the academies, the spirit of research kindled in the East. In the seventh century the Arabs rose to power, acquiring the literary stores of Greece, and during the following five centuries they became prominent in the history of science. Probably the greatest among their philosophers was the mathematician Alhazen (Hasan ibn al Hasan ibn al Haitham, Abu Ali, ca. 965–1038), an Arab of Basra.

The work of Alhazen was highly skilled and original. After he and his contemporaries abandoned the Platonic theory that vision emanated *from* the eye, he improved the existing knowledge of the optical effects of curved mirrors, the refraction of light, and Ptolemy's apparatus for measuring the angle of refraction in different media. He discovered that the angles of incidence and refraction of light were related to each other, but was unable to find the law connecting them. This was to be calculated six hundred years later, by the Dutchman Willebrord Snell. "Snell's Law," as it is now called, states that "when light passes from air to water the relation is always as 4 to 3, and when refraction occurs from air to glass the relation is as 3 to 2." This is one of the most important laws in all aspects of optical science.

Primarily a mathematician and astronomer, Alhazen also examined the anatomy of the human eye, and explained how it is we see one object with two eyes, and then not by a single ray or beam as had been previously held, but by two cones of rays proceeding from the object, one to each eye. Among nearly two hundred of his books, two contain much of the fundamental principles of optics for the first time in history. He discussed the magnifying powers of lenses, and it is possible that his observations inspired the subsequent invention of true spectacles.

Brought to Europe, these Arab works greatly influenced scientific thought there. The first European treatise on optics was written about 1270 by Vitello, or Vitellio, a native of Poland, but was not published until 1572. It was based on a Latin translation of the works of Ptolemy and Alhazen. Real advances in optics, however, were made by a contemporary of Vitello, the Franciscan friar Roger Bacon (1214–1294) who also based his studies on those of Alhazen. Although he learned much from and added much to the theories of the Arabs, Bacon erred in reverting to the Greek idea that objects are rendered visible by emanations from the eye. But he did show a much deeper appreciation of the value of experimentation in applying the principles of refraction and reflection to improvement of vision. He had a clearer, though still inaccurate, conception of the nature of a lens, and it is more than likely that he knew the nature of images formed by light entering a small orifice—the origin of the *camera obscura,* first noticed by Aristotle. Bacon is supposed to have invented the magic lantern, and he undoubtedly prophesied the vague possibility of both the telescope and the compound microscope.

The obscurity surrounding the origin of eyeglasses has never been better explained than through the discoveries of men living in the time of Bacon, and the conditions under which they were made. It is seldom that a new theory or invention is the entire work of one man; rather is it an accumulation of earlier knowledge plus a certain spark of new genius that brings the "discovery" to our attention. Also, the superstitious spirit of the Middle Ages, in which Bacon worked, probably made it necessary for an inventor of a pair of glasses or other optical instrument to hide them rather than show them to possible sponsors, or indeed to anyone, lest he draw upon himself the wrath of the church and people as a servant of the devil.

Any layman of those days, were he able to read at all, might have been startled and frightened by passages like the following from Bacon's works.

Glasses [*perspicus*] can be so constructed that objects at a very great distance appear to be quite close at hand, or conversely. Thus we may read the smallest letters from an incredible distance, number objects, however small, and can make the stars appear as near as we wish. . . . Among the more subtle powers of construction is this of directing and concentrating rays by means of [instruments of] different forms and reflections at any distance we wish, where whatsoever is subjected to them is burned. . . . But greater than such design or purpose is that the heavens might be portrayed in all their length and breadth on a corporeal figure moving with their diurnal motion, and this would be worth a whole kingdom to a wise man. . . .

Before this time, millions of short-sighted people had existed without knowing the stars, or the clouds, or what a bird looked like in flight. They were, in a sense, hopeless cripples. But man's brain was rapidly coming to the aid of his faulty eyes. There is little doubt that Bacon was the outstanding pioneer in the history of spectacles. In 1276 he alluded to them as "useful to those who are old and have weak sight." In 1285 he told all he knew about spectacles to the supposedly Italian Heinrich Goethals, the scholar known as "Doctor Solennis of Ghent," and Goethals is believed to have been at least commissioned to interview Pope Martin IV regarding them. It is probable that Goethals met Spina, a Dominican friar and friend of an Italian nobleman named D'Armato, and perhaps through the gossiping of these three men the inscription on

D'Armato's tomb, in the Church of Santa Maria Maggiore in Florence, is typical of the confusion and superstition of the times. It reads:

Here lies
Salvino degli Armatis
Died 1317
The Inventor of Spectacles
May God pardon his sins

It is true that even nowadays some people consider spectacles to be the invention of the devil. One oculist recalls a patient whom he fitted with excellent glasses, and who came back in a day or so complaining bitterly and asking for a less "powerful" pair, because now life was no longer rosy. He could see all its defects and stark reality— the cracks in the ceiling, the dirt on his friends' shirt collars, the blemishes on their faces, everything.

That spectacles probably were already in use in Europe toward the latter part of the thirteenth century, or even before, is indicated by Bernard de Gordon, the French physician who died in 1307, in his famous book the *Lilium Medicinae*, written about 1300. He calls them "berylli," and, in fact, most early glasses were cut from beryl. The modern German word for spectacles is *brille,* and the French *besicle* came from the medieval *bericle* or *berille.* The Italian dictionary of the *Accademici della Crusca* (1612) mentions a sermon by Jordan de Rivalto, published in 1305, in which he refers to the invention of spectacles as having occurred "not twenty years since."

The sixteenth century was a period of increasing intellectual activity. The need for experimental inquiry was fully realized, and the dogmas of the church and the theories of the established schools of philosophy were in question. Italy led in the science of optics, the most prominent searchers being Franciscus Maurolycus (1404–1575) of Messina, and Giambattista della Porta (1538–1615) of Naples. Maurolycus wrote a treatise which included discussions on the measurement of the intensity of light— very likely the first essay on photometry—and the optical relations of the parts of the eye, maintaining that the lens of the eye focuses on the retina, and explaining short and long sight (myopia and hyperopia), with the suggestion that the former may be corrected by concave, and the latter by convex, lenses. Among other practical applications of lenses he suggested are combinations comparable to telescopes, and one of his numerous books contains an account of binocular vision in which are found vague indications of the principles of the stereoscope, forerunner of three-dimensional slides and movies.

Toward the end of the fifteenth century the Guild of Master Spectacle Makers was formed in Nürnberg, establishing spectacle making as a trade like shoemaking or tailoring. Lenses were ground, fitted into frames, and sold on the streets to any who had money and the time to stop and try on a pair or two. (England's Worshipful Company of Spectacle Makers was chartered in 1629 and still exists.)

Most of the first spectacle makers were nothing more than fine artisans, setting new fads and fashions and pandering to the vanity of the rich. Men of high society, dignity, and learning were nearly always portrayed with spectacles before their eyes, whether or not their vision was faulty. Originally, spectacles had round lenses, and were like two reading glasses pinned together through the handles so that they could be spread in a V and held up in front of the eyes. Such glasses hang at the side of the desk in Ghirlandaio's painting of St. Jerome, and are worn with weirdly dramatic effect in the Florentine engraving of the same period which supposedly shows the ritual murder of St. Simon of Trent.

In the seventeenth century dark-rimmed glasses were fashionable in Spain, and a pair was always placed on the theatrical mask of Zerbino, one of the Spanish characters of early Italian comedy. The Flemish painter de Herdt, of the same period, shows in his portrait of a woman counting money that spectacles had changed from the first scissored style and the early tic-on type to "nose-pinchers." Not until two centuries later were single "spyglasses" to become popular, at which time pince-nez eyeglasses were worn swinging on chains around the neck like the watches that women carried. Some interesting prints showing these nineteenth-century eyeglass fashions can be seen in the print room of the Metropolitan Museum in New York, and in the same museum there is a painting of Cardinal Don Fernando Niño de Guevara by El Greco (1575), in which the cardinal wears the earlier type of spectacles with loops around his ears. In a recent exhibition at the Museum of the City of New York an old pocket knife was displayed containing several curious blades and a small pair of spectacles.

In spite of the formation of the guilds, spectacle making did not become an industry of much importance until the invention of printing, in 1440, made more of the common people aware of the need to correct their visual errors. However, the majority could not read or write, and the cost of glasses remained prohibitive. When most of the guilds were eliminated, peddlers became the chief source of glasses for the general public. They traveled all through the land with their imperfect wares in open boxes strung around their necks. Optical stores did not come into being in Europe until the end of the seventeenth century, and in America at the beginning of the eighteenth.

Leonardo da Vinci (1452–1519) did much to advance the science of optics when he added it to the many others improved by his special genius. He used to lie on his back on a summer's day, looking up into the green leafy branches of the trees above his head, and note how flat they looked until he moved his head slowly from side to side, when they took on a three-dimensional effect. He was quick to experiment, and one of his many diagrams illustrates the action of convex spectacle lenses. He thought that the difficulty of vision would be eased by making the objects appear farther off, thus lessening the need for converging the eyes. This same principle of eye divergence is employed in modern binoculars which, the width of the eyes apart at one end, diverge the line of vision at the other end by means of prisms, so that the eyes look around the edges of the distant object, seeing more and making it appear larger and consequently nearer.

Little is known about how lens powers were designated in the sixteenth century, when concave lenses for the correction of myopia first came into use. Nowadays, lens prescriptions are made up with great exactitude, after minutely careful examination of the patient. In 1875 the international scale of measurement in "diopters" was adopted. This followed a suggestion made by Nagel in 1866 for the use of the metric system for measuring and designating the power of lenses, in place of the English inch system then in use. The term "diopter," proposed by a Frenchman named Monoyer, is now universally used to designate the dioptric or refractive power of a lens of one meter (39.37 inches) equivalent of focal length. But in the old days about the only gauge for lenses was the age of the would-be purchaser, and lenses were accordingly classified

as "young" spectacles—probably meaning weak concave
lenses—and "older" spectacles, meaning strong plus.

The seventeenth century was a period of intense activity
and progress in the optical field. The phenomenon of
diffraction was discovered by the Italian Jesuit, Francesco
Maria Grimaldi (ca. 1618–1663). Diffraction is the spreading out, or dividing from the strictly rectilinear path, of
light passing through a small aperture or around the edge
of an opaque object. Then, in 1623, the earliest illustrated
scientific work on the use of spectacles was written by
Daza de Valdes (Benito), a notary of the Inquisition at
Seville. In this work de Valdes mentions "cataract" lenses
as an aid to the human lens, or its capsule, which has become so opaque through the disease of cataract as to ob-
struct the passage of light waves to the retina. Probably
in no other eye affliction is it more necessary to exercise
care, tact, and judgment than in the fitting of glasses for
cataract, and even today it is extremely difficult, requiring
all the skill and knowledge of the refractionist, the optician,
and the lens manufacturer combined in perfect teamwork.

A strong interest in astronomy grew in the seventeenth
century, and with the popularization of the telescope by
Galileo Galilei the attendant problems in grinding suitable
lenses gave a fresh impetus to the profession.

The word telescope, from the Greek meaning "far view,"
was invented by the famous Greek scholar Demiscianus,
at the request of the president of the Lyncean Academy,

Prince Cesi. It was used by Galileo as early as 1612, but was not introduced into England until much later, trunk or cylinder being the terms employed there before.

Galileo was not the inventor of the telescope, as is often claimed. The first binocular telescope, consisting of two telescopes placed side by side, was constructed in 1608 by an obscure optician of Middelburg named Hans Lippershey, the inventor of the ordinary or Dutch telescope. The subject was then taken up by the monks. A rumor of the new invention which reached Venice in June of 1609 was sufficient to set Galileo on the track, and, after only one night's profound meditation on the principles of refraction, he produced a telescope of threefold magnifying power. He even improved upon this improvement of Lippershey's original telescope until he attained to a power of thirty-two, and his instruments, which he manufactured with his own hands, were soon in request all over Europe.

Astronomers know that the earth, wrapped in its jacket of atmosphere, is not a very satisfactory place from which to study the stars. On a clear night, or day for that matter, the atmosphere seems to be transparent and the visibility extremely good, but this is not really so. Just as fishes' eyes were made to see through water, so have our human eyes evolved for use in air. We see by means of light that penetrates the atmosphere, an atmosphere which before the radiation from sun or stars reaches it is an opaque black ocean.

Most modern astronomical observations are made by means of photographic telescopes which are left openly staring at the same point for hours and hours on end, thus enabling them to pick up, however fuzzily, distant objects too faint to be seen by the naked eye. But sometimes the human eye is much quicker than the photographic machine, catching fine details before they move and blur. For this reason, many astronomers prefer to observe the planets through direct vision, without any mechanical aid, although this method is obsolete for other kinds of astronomy. A compromise may be reached, and less fuzzy pictures obtained in spite of movement, through motion-picture telescopes, and a plan was formulated to take such movies of Mars with the Palomar telescope during that planet's near approach to earth in 1956.

Among the several learned Dutchmen of the seventeenth century who devoted much of their time to the study of light and optical instruments was one named Christian Huygens, who was born at The Hague in 1629 but whose best work dates from the time he became a resident of France, upon the suggestion of Louis XIV, in 1666. Huygens' principles of motion greatly assisted his famous English contemporary Sir Isaac Newton in formulating his law of gravitation, and also the laws governing the phenomena of color production by thin films, now known as Newton's rings, and the theory of the formation of images which is extremely important in all modern optical-instrument systems. One of Newton's books, *Opticks*, ranks high among the most important of its kind.

Huygens was a pioneer in the study of polarized light, which resulted from his experiments with double refraction in Iceland Spar crystals, and he also greatly improved the grinding of spherical lenses. He experimented with compound eyepieces, that is with more than one lens, which had been previously suggested by Eustachio Divini.

It was probably about this time that the compound type of microscope first came into common use, making possible the science of bacteriology. It began with Antoni van Leeuwenhoek, who was born in Delft on October 24, 1632. In a letter to a contemporary scientist, van Leeuwenhoek described the first living microorganisms to be seen by man, in September 1675. He wrote of "animalcules in rain water that were ten thousand times smaller than the animalcules seen by Swammerdam and named water-fleas." Jan Swammerdam was the contemporary Dutch naturalist who devised the method of studying the circulatory system by means of injections. Leeuwenhoek made his own microscopes, very simply, and at his death he had completed 247 of them, and had designed 419 lenses, mostly very small double convex ones mounted between two plates made of silver, gold, or brass.

For the origin of sunglasses the records go back to the latter part of the sixteenth century, when colored glass was first used for protection against glare. The earliest reference is to green glass lenses manufactured in 1561 in England; blue lenses in 1672; smoked glasses in 1767; amber in 1832. In America the making of amethyst glasses obtained from windows tinted by long exposure to the elements was suggested, in Philadelphia, in 1885.

The psychological reaction of different people to bright light varies very much—some love it, others fear it. There is no real cause for fear, as only intensely bright light can damage the eyes. The ultraviolet rays in sunshine reflected from snow can cause a very painful condition called "snow blindness" which sometimes takes several days to clear up. It is due to the rays' destroying some of the cells in the cornea, and not to the effect of light on the retina. Another result of snow reflection, which in this case penetrates farther into the eye, is often experienced by mountain climbers, and also people recovering from a cataract operation—a tendency to see everything as pink. This is called erythropia, or red vision, and calls for immediate reduction of the light, when the effect will wear off.

To alleviate the ill effects of snow upon the eyes, Eskimos have for many ages worn hollow wooden or ivory goggles tied around their heads with leather sinews or string. Light enters only through a small horizontal slit in each eyepiece, and the inside of the goggles is smoked, or otherwise darkened, to further reduce the glare.

It has been known for some time, then, that vision can be protected, and even improved, by small round or slit-like openings in devices worn on the face. In 1551, in Venice, slits in visors of knights' armor were recommended for dueling and battle, and in many places masks were created to aid cross- or wall-eyed people by forcing the faulty eyes to assume a normal position in order to see at all through the apertures, which varied according to whether the deviation was convergent or divergent. But it was not until about 1844 that prisms were first recommended for the cure of what are called "squints."

There is no blanket rule for the use of dark glasses. In certain diseased conditions of the eye, they may have to be prescribed, but otherwise it is not always a good idea to wear them, as a vicious circle may be started whereby the less light one sees the less one wants, until finally it seems pleasant to put them on even on dull days. Generally speaking, they are essential only on high snow, tropic deserts or seas, and in unshaded places such as the drier parts of Australia.

Modern conditions, often including long periods of application to close work under the most exacting conditions, and the greatly increased use of artificial illumination of high intensity, subject the eyes to a strain that nature never intended. Among the best lenses produced today to alleviate these conditions are those made of Soft-Lite glass, which is especially designed to absorb glare and relieve eyestrain. It tones down the intensity of the light, yet it is inconspicuous on the wearer and is not habit-forming.

Benjamin Franklin, among his many other achievements, made one great contribution to the science of optics. In 1784 he invented bifocal glasses. He described his invention with simple modesty in letters he wrote to George Whately: "I cannot distinguish a letter, even of large print, but am happy in the invention of double spectacles, which, serving for distant objects as well as near ones, make my eyes as useful to me as ever they were. . . ." "I imagine it will be found pretty generally true that the same convexity of glass, through which a man sees clearest and best at the distance for proper reading, is not the best for greater distances. . . . I therefore had formerly two pair of spectacles, which I shifted occasionally as in travelling. I sometimes read and often wanted to regard the prospects. Finding this change troublesome and not always sufficiently ready, I had the glasses cut and half of each kind associated in the same circle. By this means, as I wear my spectacles constantly, I have only to move my eyes up or down as I want to see distinctly far or near, the proper glasses being always ready."

Of the many types of bifocal lenses that have been made since Franklin's day, only the modern fused and one-piece forms, and to a limited extent the "cemented wafer" types, have survived. The difference between the early bifocals and the modern types are principally in appearance and permanence. Most modern bifocals resemble single-vision lenses so closely that no casual observer will be able to distinguish them as bifocals. Their polished glass surfaces have no place where dust can lodge, and the lenses never come apart.

Bifocals are now available in an astonishing variety to suit practically every requirement. For example, the well-known American optical-instrument manufacturers, Bausch and Lomb, were recently called upon to make bifocals for a symphony orchestra violinist. He wanted, for his right eye, a half-moon segment put in the upper outer section of the right glass, near the temple, and for his left eye a similar segment in the upper inside section of the glass, near the nose. Equipped this way, when he had his chin on his violin and looked down he could see the music through the lower and middle parts of his glasses, and did not have to move his head to see his conductor's gestures, merely needing to raise his eyes upward and to the right to look through the inserted segments, which accommodated his sight for distance. This same firm also makes trifocals, and even quadrifocals for correcting sight at four distances. With the trifocals, the wearer, supposing he is engaged in work such as watchmaking, can do close work in fine detail by looking through the lower section of his glasses, select a tool from a nearby shelf by using the central section, and recognize a customer coming through a distant door with the upper part. About two hundred and fifty pairs of these highly specialized glasses for various trades and professions are turned out each week.

A great forward step was made in the use of lenses for the correction of errors of refraction when, in 1801, the English scientist Thomas Young demonstrated the condition of astigmatism. An English astronomer, George Airy by name, corrected this defect in his own eye by means of a sphero-cylindrical lens made under his direction by the optician Fuller of Ipswich in 1827.

Before this time, there were few means by which the lenses used in spectacles could be properly checked to establish correct refraction and dispersion of light. Then Joseph von Fraunhofer, of Munich (1787–1826), developed exact methods of testing surfaces by means of Newton's rings, a system which is extensively used today in the manufacture of lenses.

The next important contribution to optics was something which you can see today, in an improved version, whenever you go to have your eyes examined. In 1851 the German Hermann von Helmholtz (he who once said that if he were offered a human eye as an optical apparatus he would reject it) invented the ophthalmoscope, an instrument with a mirror centrally perforated for viewing the interior of the eye, especially the retina. Von Helmholtz also gave the first definition of color-blindness. He was, in fact, the highest authority, in his field, of the nineteenth century.

Even as recently as a hundred years ago, buying a pair of eyeglasses was usually a matter of trial and error, not much advanced from the ignorance of the Middle Ages, and within many families living today some of the older members may recall people going down the street to the five-and-ten-cent store to get a new pair of specs because their old ones had "worn out."

In purchasing glasses a well-fitting frame set at the right angle and at the correct distance from the eyes is as important as a correct lens, and the material used in making the frames must be carefully considered. For about five hundred years from the beginning of the fourteenth century, frames were made mostly of horn, but after that came comfortably light gold and rimless frames. Today, for no valid reason unless it be the whim of fashion or the high cost of gold, we have reverted to heavy horn or shell rims, though the latest trend is toward lighter plastics resembling shell.

Compared to the hit-or-miss bits of glass that were used as lenses by the peddlers of early glasses, the careful selection and manufacture of modern lenses is amazing. Among the many different types of spectacles and lenses in current use there are five which are the most usual: spectacles for constant wear—these are for people who have not yet reached the age where the eye becomes normally presbyopic (unable to see near objects clearly), and who are too short-sighted, long-sighted, or astigmatic to get along

without them; spectacles for children, as part of the treat-
ment of a "squint"; spectacles for distance only; spectacles
for close work only; bifocal spectacles and reversible spectacles—these latter are for presbyopes who have only one
eye. The distance lens is put in one side of the spectacles,
the reading lens in the other, and the frames are especially
made to allow the wearer to take them off and turn them
around.

Of the four more ordinary lenses, plane lenses are flat
and cheap, and do not scratch easily if laid down without
a case (glasses should never be put down with the glass
downward, however); toric lenses are curved and give a
wider field of clear definition, but being curved forward
they scratch easily and sometimes give annoying reflections; cemented bifocals are plane or toric lenses for distance with a small segment stuck onto the lower part for
reading—if the patient does not like them, the stuck-on
bit can be removed, leaving a pair of ordinary distance
glasses; solid and fused bifocals are all in one piece and
look very nice because the line between the distance and
reading portions hardly shows, but they are more ex-
pensive than the cemented ones.

One of the latest achievements in scientific lens design
is the Orthogon—a series of corrected, wide-vision ophthalmic lenses designed to give the wearer clear and distinct vision through every part of the lens area to which
the eye may turn, even in bifocals. This is accomplished

by selecting for each power of lens those particular curves which will eliminate the astigmatic variation between center and margin of the lens area.

Then there are the contact lenses. Many people consider these as a vain person's substitute for spectacles, but actually they are for diseases which cannot be helped much by spectacles. Contact lenses are thin shells of glass or plastic which fit over the cornea inside the lids. It is difficult to make them so that they can be worn for any length of time with comfort. They are separated from the cornea by a thin layer of fluid (tears or salt solution), and their action is pretty much that of fishes' eyes seeing under water. The glass, the patient's cornea, and his aqueous are all of about the same optical density, so that the only bending of the light rays will be where they leave the air and enter the glass, which can be made to any desired curve. These lenses are very good as a substitute for an irregular, scarred cornea which, being inside the glass, no longer affects the path of light rays. (The action is similar to that which occurs if you fill up the irregularities in a piece of opaque ground glass by wetting it, thus making it transparent.) Sometimes the improvement in sight through the wearing of contact lenses is almost unbelievable.

Glass eyes are not such a new idea, although today they are made to look so natural and fit so comfortably that they are truly works of art. The fine attention to matching detail and color is almost miraculous—anything can be achieved with modern methods. There is an amusing story of a one-eyed New Yorker who owns a set of glass eyes of progressive degrees of tiredness. When he attends a heavy business meeting or a boring party he discreetly changes his glass eye from time to time to match the growing tiredness of his real eye. The thirteenth eye, in place of the iris, has an unfurled American flag.

Ophthalmic glass used exclusively for eyeglasses is generally known as optical glass because of the high precision demanded of it, and the necessity of maintaining accurate control over the entire manufacturing process. The requirements are very definite and rigid, and in general are quite different from those of optical glass used for prisms and lenses in microscopes and other optical instruments. There are fourteen possible faults to guard against during the manufacture of spectacle lenses, and some twenty-five different types of optical glass in use today, from which it can be seen that enormous progress has been made in optics since those medieval days of ignorance, superstition, and fear. Man has improved his vision so that with the aid of instruments which are children of his brain he can now see into the deepest of nature's secrets—stars which lie at almost incomprehensibly far distances from the earth, microscopic channels of water coursing between individual grains of sand.

If the pioneers in the science of optics, men such as Galileo and Huygens, were to see some of the latest optical instruments in one of our great modern laboratories, if they were to study the very newest inventions—some still only in the drafting-board stage—which are being designed to aid man in his next stage of evolution, the conquest of space, they might not recognize the results of their original findings, might not believe their eyes.

Chapter 11

EYES IN SPACE

If man is soon to travel in outer space, he will have to invent adequate protection for his eyes. He may make his home in this new environment—as different from earth as dry land from the sea—long before his eyes have had anything like the immense amount of time needed for them to change and adapt naturally. To avoid the danger of blindness from the dazzling contrast between total light and total darkness, found in space where a gentling atmosphere is completely lacking, future man must learn again how to use his eyes.

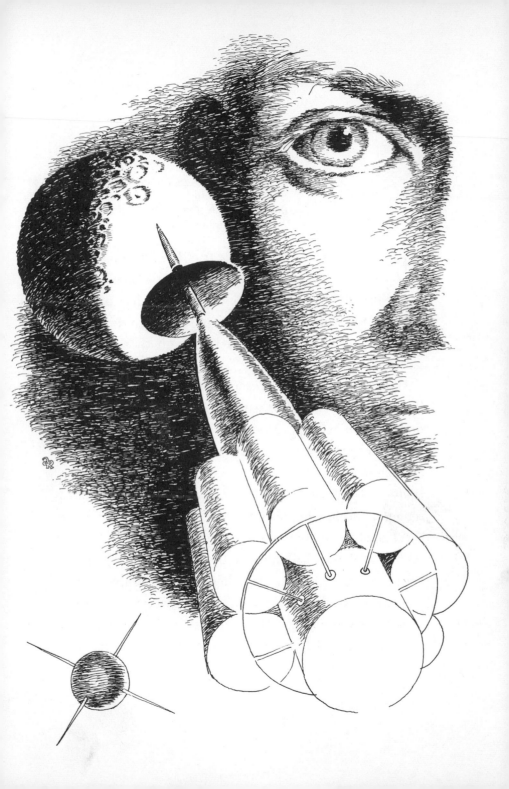

PETER: *I only want to look around a bit. There's
so much to see.
Ah, peace on earth, I'm a boy for the sights.*
—Christopher Fry, A *Sleep of Prisoners*

E ARLY one evening not long after the beginning of the
Age of Space, Quartermaster Jairus stood on his
signal bridge of a Space Force observation ship, anchored
near shore, watching and listening to the international
police satellites as they hurtled through the heavens at
various altitudes.

With their television eyes and film-fed brains, the satellites constantly stored or sent out reports about conditions
on earth, in the upper atmosphere, and in outer space.
Clear and precise, the reports included information concerning magnetic fields, micro-meteors, gravity, star radiations, and optical properties of the upper regions. Jairus
remembered hearing his father tell about the time, before
the launching of the first satellite, when only a little of
such knowledge had filtered down faintly through the
ocean of atmosphere to the comparatively simple recording machines on earth—when human awareness of space
conditions was almost as limited as that of a fish about air.

When the quartermaster had entered the Space Force

Naval Observation Corps his eyesight had been put through severe tests, similar to those used by the regular Navy. Among other things, he had been requested to identify objects of various types as they appeared far to port or starboard, at the same time keeping his gaze fixed steadily ahead; he had been tested for distant and close focusing, for color-blindness, and for his blind spot.

This blind spot was not an affliction peculiar to Jairus. We all have blind spots; they are perfectly normal. When your eyes are in motion they are always stone blind, and you will never be able to see them actually move. You may look at their reflection in a mirror and turn your head from side to side, keeping your eyes fixed upon their image in the glass, which may give you an illusion of seeing them in motion, but of course it is only your head that moves.

The blind spot provides proof that the eye is only the somewhat imperfect means by which we receive reflections of the world about us, being in itself incapable of perceiving anything whatsoever. Proper vision is formed not within the eye but in the brain, where it is controlled by the intellect. (Webster defines intellect as "the power or faculty of knowing as distinguished from the power to feel and to will—especially the power of reasoning, judging, comprehending, etc.")

In our eyes, the blind spot occurs at the point of entry at the rear of the eyeball of the optic nerve. This entrance point, being one end of the nerve "cable," contains no

visual cells, neither rods nor cones, and consequently cannot react to stimuli as does the surrounding retina.

As we look at objects within our visual field, the blind
spot appears as an empty space which becomes larger the
farther we project it out into the world. The actual space
the blind spot occupies in the eye is only 1.5 millimeters,
but at a distance of ten inches from the eye it becomes as
large as a postage stamp, at three feet the size of a fist, at
four yards larger than a human head, and at twenty yards
larger than a horse—yet we are usually unaware of its
existence because we regard things rather rapidly with
two eyes, and under normal circumstances the right eye
overlooks the gap in the left visual field, and the left eye
that in the right field.

Paradoxically, the blind spot is often the cause of our
seeing more than is actually there. For example, if you
close one eye and look at the space between two black
bars drawn close to one another horizontally, and then
move your head from side to side until it reaches a certain
position, the space will vanish and the two bars appear as
one long bar. From this it can be seen that our eyes, at
least when used one at a time, are not always to be believed. The blind spot not only is a physical phenomenon
based upon the defective optical mechanism of the human
eye, but is also a psychological process, because the brain
is baffled by it. It must be stressed, however, that the blind

spot is not a physical defect brought about by accident or disease, but occurs in every normal eye.

There are about 15,000,000 people in the world who are actually blind, of which an estimated 308,000 are in the United States. It is only when we lose our sight, if only for a brief period, that we fully realize the value of what we usually take for granted. A newly blinded person, learning to go on living with his affliction, knows the humiliation, the difficulty, and often the physical pain of attempting to discover the relationship in space between him and even the most common objects. After a while he will develop his "sixth sense" (a stepping up of that proprioceptive sense discussed in Chapter 7), becoming aware of his approach to a wall or chair or anything else through a faint emanation, a change in the small sounds caused by his own movements and their rebound from other surfaces. His dark new world takes on various "patterns" in sound and touch sense. A Seeing-Eye dog is of little or no use to anyone in whom a slight vestige of sight remains, because the visual patterns of owner and dog usually conflict.

There is one thing peculiar to human eyes—that is to say, not found in the eyes of lower animals—which is called dominancy and serviency. In man, the two eyes do not contribute equally to the formation of the single picture realized by the brain. In a right-handed person the right eye provides almost all of the picture, in a left-handed person it is the left eye that does this. In other words, in the majority of human beings the brain looks out through the dominant window on the right-hand side of the face, with the subservient left-hand window adding only a little extra information.

As a direct result of modern conditions, particularly among city dwellers, eyes are becoming elongated and more and more shortsighted, their work from early childhood generally being limited to looking not much farther than across a room or street. These easy habits do not exercise the eyes sufficiently to help them withstand the increased strain put upon them by the muscular tension necessary for close-range focusing, or convergence. The eyeballs give way under the pressure, their position of rest being permanently adapted for the perception of nearby objects. Nearsightedness is definitely on the increase among civilized races, developing in childhood, and it is hereditary.

A normal, young eye, in order to see objects clearly at various distances, accommodates by a tautening or relaxing of the ciliary body and the tough, elastic capsule which suspends the lens in position and holds its shape. Such an eye, for example, can immediately read the signs on an approaching bus at about two hundred feet.

As it grows older, the human lens changes in two ways—in color and in elasticity. Crystal-clear at first, it yellows with age as one of its proteins becomes less soluble and more opaque. This tends to reduce the passage of light through the eye, particularly blue light, so that a septuagenarian receives only fifteen per cent of blue light compared to ninety per cent in a child's eye. Incidentally, this will often make the matching of shades of blue a matter of blind argument between young and old.

With the second change in the lens, the loss of elasticity —which progresses at the same rate throughout life for almost everyone with healthy eyes—the ability to focus at close range lessens. At the age of six, the nearest point at which a normal eye can see in clear detail is about 2.4 inches away. At thirty years of age it is usually four inches, at forty the distance increases to six inches, and at fifty to ten inches. After seventy, the lens becomes hard and inelastic and cannot focus clearly at any distance. This state, called presbyopia from two Greek words meaning "old" and "eye," is not a disease but is simply the normal hardening of the lens, just as arteries harden with old age. When first noticed, the person concerned often fears that his or her eyes have "worn out," but eyes do not wear out. Like any other part of the body, they must be constantly exercised to remain healthy, and, even so, the range of vision will change with increasing age, but not to the point of blindness unless complications set in.

Eyesight has more to do with chosen ways of life than is commonly realized. Just as it affects the habits of the lower animals, so does it control human lives. The short-sighted (myopic) child is likely to take to scholarly professions or to close work that entails attention to minute detail, whereas longsighted (hyperopic) children tend to become outdoor men and women of action. It is often possible to tell whether or not a child needs corrective glasses by simply watching him at play, judging from the degree of ease with which he catches a thrown ball—provided, of course, that he is not hindered by some other physical defect. This should be ascertained by the family physician, before the child is taken to have his eyes examined by an oculist. If the physician finds nothing else wrong, he will probably send the child to a reputable oculist who will carefully study his case before prescribing the type of glasses needed. A reliable optician will then make the glasses exactly according to the oculist's prescription, and will give the child fittings until he is satisfied that the glasses are properly balanced and are set at the right distance from the ends of the eyelashes.

It is almost impossible to tell whether or not a baby is born shortsighted. The baby has no way of telling us just how well it sees, but unless it is obviously blind or abnormal symptoms appear there is seldom any need to worry about its eyes for the first six months. It cannot see clearly at birth, and even the color of its eyes will not be established for half a year. It takes time for a baby to learn to converge both eyes simultaneously, to focus, and to see in three dimensions. This is why parents often wonder if their child is developing a squint, because now and then the eyes do not move together in the same direction. Probably it will be six years before the child attains perfect binocular vision. When a child begins to read, it is preferable to give him lettered blocks or books with very large type, as his powers of convergence for close vision are not yet fully developed, and if the type is too small he will invariably hold the book too close to his eyes in an instinctive but futile effort to focus properly.

This matter of going to the proper person immediately anything seems wrong with your eyes is of the utmost importance. Probably there is no part of the human body that is more valuable and yet is treated more casually, by most people, than the eyes. When a tiny cinder blows into the eye, or a similar common occurrence takes place, most people think it silly to make a fuss; ordinarily a person just tries to rub a cinder out. Obviously, this is the wrong thing to do. Under a microscope, foreign bodies that lodge in the eye are generally seen to be many-faceted, jagged bits of material, and, minute as each of the dagger points is, any one of them can abrase or even cut the surface of the cornea, leaving a pit which invites infection. In more cases than is generally known, this leads to serious trouble. "Rubbing the other eye" to flood the cinder out with tears, or going to the nearest druggist to have the cinder removed, really belong in the category of old wives' tales, with all due respect to druggists. The cinder may come out

with such treatments, and the pain may stop, but the fact
is that damage may have been done to the eyeball, no
matter how small, and it is this that has to be properly
treated. The ideal thing to do is to go at once to a physician, preferably one who is also an oculist, but do not
ever permit a well-meaning friend or relative, a pharma-
cist, or an optician to attempt extraction of the foreign
matter.

Julian Huxley maintains that evolution is now of small
importance to man. The lower animals are evolving continually, but so slowly that they are being left far behind.
Comparatively speaking, the progress of man, now more
social than physical, is taking place with the speed of
lightning. However, if he is not to be swamped by his own
inventive powers, his brain power must continue to develop rapidly, sweeping away old taboos and opening
freely to new vistas. Civilization—a universal sense of
values and good taste, balance and rhythm—must "evolve"
just as plants and animals have evolved physically.

Apart from the natural blind spots in our eyes, many of
us remain blind to a number of things that could add to
our civilization and to our personal pleasure and good.
Civilization is an achievement of the mind, and conversely
it is a means to a good state of mind. It is not entirely de-
pendent upon the beauties of the fine arts or the wonders
of thought, scientific or otherwise. It is also made up of

such things as sun, rain, bread, wine, a spring breeze ruffling freshly green trees, the expression on an aware face, microscopic miracles. If we have eyes to see, and the curiosity to explore from each new discovery on and on along its attendant chain of wonder and delight, it is unlikely that we will ever be useless or lonely or at a loss for something truly exciting and satisfying to do. The main necessity for a highly civilized person is not that he be creative but that he be appreciative, sharing his appreciation with others, and always gaily, for no truly civilized person is somber.

If man is not to die out, certain changes must occur in his body, particularly in his lungs and eyes, to meet new conditions. Because of dominancy and serviency in his eyesight, and because his field of vision is becoming narrower, it is possible that in time his two eyes will merge into one Cyclopean orb placed in the middle of his face.

At present our binocular and stereoscopic vision is being gradually destroyed, partly as the price we pay for our speech center, but the single orb of the future will very likely regain these powers by developing two foveas, just as some birds alive today have two foveas and so stereoscopic vision in each eye.

The eye of tomorrow may possibly be both microscopic and telescopic, extremely aware of motion and color, and with great clarity of focus. Two-eyed, present-day man has no need of such microscopic delicacy in his vision—in fact, it would be a handicap, since it would not enable him to judge distances correctly and avoid objects at a convenient distance. Man has made for himself temporary makeshifts to compensate for this lack in his vision—microscopes, telescopes, and so forth by which he can add considerably to his speculative knowledge. Perhaps the most important change to come will be the ability of eyes to perceive as light many forms of energy known to exist today but which make no impression on the present human retina.

If we are to travel habitually in outer space, as many believe we will, certain adjustments will have to be made to allow eyes to withstand even ordinary light there. On the earth's surface only about three-quarters of the light comes directly from the sun—the remainder, diffused by the atmosphere, strikes into the shadows to make visible those objects which are not directly reached by sunlight. In outer space, with no swaddling atmosphere to diffuse it, sunlight is infinitely more powerful than on earth. The sky is not blue, it is ebony black, and the only light that reaches into the inky shadows cast by objects in the blazing sunlight is starlight, which is too weak to be caught by the human retina as it is today constructed. Consequently the contrast between light and shade in outer space is so tremendous as to be devastating to human eyes. The pupil of the eye, accommodated to the blackness of the sky around, will be wide open, so that if a man should glance for even a split second at the sun, or the sunlit earth or moon, he would be in danger of blindness. The windows of space-ships, so the space doctors tell us, could be provided with special glass to alleviate the glare, but if a man outside a spaceship, and not protected by any special device, were to look at objects in the full brilliance of that awful sunshine his pupils would shrink to pinpoints. Everything in shadow would become completely invisible. He might even imagine himself to be without hands or feet, if these parts of him were not reached by light.

It is not easy for us to visualize such conditions, or to allow the possibility that mechanical eyes, such as our present television instruments, might do the work for us. We instinctively, or perhaps more through habit, resent the idea of giving up our two beautiful eyes for strange substitutes, either physical or mechanical, finding it hard to believe that these could ever properly convey to us new wonders or those cherished things we look for daily.

Perhaps it may help us forward a little if we bear in mind that it is our wonderful brain that really gives us our thoughts and sensations, and that so long as we have *some* kind of receiving apparatus for the sights around us—any kind, so long as it functions properly in existing conditions —we will not miss anything and may gain much. The windows of the soul should not be limited to the eyes. Although the form our visual organs may take in the far-distant future is a controversial subject, there is little doubt that the cosmos we will then perceive will be very

different and will need looking at in a very different **way.**
Man is already perfecting for himself a protective, complete covering for use in outer space, somewhat reminiscent of the outer skeletons, or shells, of the early scorpion-
like sea creatures, and including a special transparent
section for clear vision. It will probably be many millenniums before man's physical eyes, among other vital
organs, adapt fully to meet, unaided, the challenges of
outer space. It may take him considerably less time to
become accustomed to the everyday handling of mechanical instruments functioning as eyes, or to the constant
wearing of such artificial eyes until they actually seem to
become part of himself—a newly evolved improvement
to meet a new environment in which, at first, he might be
considered comparable to the first amphibians on earth.

The sea had developed a heavy swell at sundown, so
that Quartermaster Jairus had to steady himself against
the bridge rail as he studied the skies through powerful
binoculars, which had been polished and repolished until
miniature rainbows hung about them. Conditions were
favorable. He concentrated on the moon, on that particular mountain ring known as Archimedes, between the
main ridge of the Apennine Mountains and the great lunar
lava plain, the Sea of Storms. In the center of Archimedes
he could just make out the reddish patch, like a bull's-eye,
which marked the huge relay space station from which a

message had come recently requesting replenishment of certain food, medicines, and equipment. It was part of the quartermaster's job to see that such requests were properly filled, and to ascertain space conditions before and during the flight of the freight and mail rockets.

After a glance at his electric wrist watch, Jairus picked up the radio telephone and checked with the shore depot on final details for the launching of the freight rocket to the moon. Everything was set. The lading papers were in order, and all international permissions cleared. In a few seconds, the supplies would be on their way.

With the approach of night, the sea had dimmed through an anonymous gray to deep indigo. Along the horizon, the day still lingered, but above it the sky was dark. Jairus and the other men concerned, on ship and shore, readied their eyes and instruments for the launching. Over the loudspeakers came a mechanical counting: ". . . five . . . four . . . three . . . two . . . one . . . *zero.*"

A burst of ruddy flame flared from the multistaged rocket as, in a cascading thunder of sound, it rose upon its flight. For a few seconds, Jairus and the rest of the crew watched its glowing pink trail. Then, picking up speed, it disappeared from sight. No eye could tell where it was in the blackness of the night. Each observer's brain told him that it was there, somewhere, soaring away and away on its mission, but only hope and faith held their eyes turned steadily upward.

Suddenly the rocket, passing beyond the shadow of the earth, flashed, sun-gilded, into sight once more, to be lost again, almost immediately, as it entered those distant upper regions where the stars no longer twinkle, but glow like animal eyes in the dark.

In due course, a message reached Jairus from the moon, reporting the safe arrival of the supplies. The space freighter had successfully penetrated upward to its destination, assisting in another step of our journey to the stars, a journey which, billions of years ago, began when a beam of light pierced downward through darkness to create life and vision on earth.

Bibliography

Index

Bibliography

BOOKS

Bartley, S. Howard. *Vision.* New York: Van Nostrand, 1941.

Colbert, Edwin H. *Evolution of the Vertebrates.* New York: John Wiley and Sons, 1955.

Davenport, Millia. *The Book of Costume.* New York: Crown, 1948.

Hamilton, W. J.; Boyd, J. D.; Mossman, H. W. *Human Embryology.* Baltimore: Williams & Wilkins, 1952.

Howard, Len. *Birds as Individuals.* New York: Doubleday, 1953.

Jones, Sir Harold Spencer. *Life on Other Worlds.* New York: Macmillan, 1940; New American Library, 1956.

Kahn, Fritz. *Man in Structure and Function.* New York: Knopf, 1943.

Kalmus, H. *Genetics.* London: Penguin, 1947.

Leonard, J. Norton. *Flight into Space.* New York: Random House, 1953.

Mann, Ida, and Pirie, Antoinette. *The Science of Seeing.* London: Penguin, 1950.

Moore, Ruth. *Man, Time, and Fossils.* New York: Knopf, 1953.

Romer, Alfred Sherwood. *The Vertebrate Body.* Philadelphia: W. B. Saunders Company, second edition, 1955.

Simpson, George Gaylord. *Life of the Past.* New Haven, Connecticut: Yale University Press, 1953.

———. *The Meaning of Evolution.* New Haven, Connecticut: Yale University Press, 1949.

Smith, Homer W. *Kamongo, or The Lungfish and the Padre.* New York: Viking, 1932; Compass, 1956.

Teale, Edwin Way. *Grassroot Jungles.* New York: Dodd, Mead, 1945.

Walls, Gordon L. *The Vertebrate Eye.* Bloomfield Hills, Michigan: Cranbrook Institute of Science, 1942.

ARTICLES

Gesell, Arnold. "Infant Vision." *Scientific American,* February 1950.

Reesin, Austen H. "Arrested Vision." *Scientific American,* July 1950.

Singer, Charles. "The Advent of the Lens." *Technology Review,* April 1933.

Bausch and Lomb Publications. New York: Bausch and Lomb Optical Company, 1956.

Index